CHEMISTRY

F. O. Harriss M.A.
Head of Chemistry Department, Malvern College

H. J. C. Ferguson M.A., Ph.D.
Malvern College
Formerly Head of Chemistry Department

LONGMAN

Acknowledgements

We are grateful to the following for permission to reproduce photographs; British Petroleum, Figs 2.7 and 14.2; British Rail Research, 10.2 (a); Building Research Establishment, Crown ©, reproduced by permission of the Controller of Her Majesty's Stationery Office, 9.9; J. Allan Cash Photolibrary, 1.2, 9.8, 10.1 and 14.7 (b); Environmental Picture Library, 14.5; *Farmer's Weekly*, 6.2; Geoscience Features Picture Library, 9.6 (a and b) and 9.10; ICCE/Philip Steele, 7.2; Inland Steel Company, 11.3 and 14.7 (a); Ann Ronan Picture Library, 4.9 and 15.3; Royal Institution, 13.4; Scotch Whisky Association/Anthony James, 2.9; Science Photo Library/John Howard, 14.7 (d); Thames Water, 7.3, . 7.4 and 14.7 (c); Thermit Welding, 10.2 (b); University of Technology, Loughborough, 14.6; Zinc Development Association, 7.7.

Figures 1.3, 1.5, 1.6, 5.1, 6.1, 8.3, 10.6 and 15.1 were taken by Andrew Lambert.

Cover photo of lightening over Waskesiu Prince Albert National Park, Saskatchewan, Canada by The Photo Source–Daily Telegraph.

CHEMISTRY

Longman Science 11–14

General Editor: John L. Lewis O.B.E.

Also in the series:
Biology   0 582 018668
Physics   0 582 01865 X
Biology Teacher's Guide   0 582 093732
Chemistry Teacher's Guide   0 582 093724
Physics Teacher's Guide   0 582 093740

Longman Group UK Limited
Longman House, Burnt Mill, Harlow, Essex,
CM20 2JE, England
and Associated Companies throughout the World.

First published 1983
Second edition 1991
Third impression 1992
ISBN 0 582 018633

Set in 11/12pt Univers Light Linotron 202
Printed in Great Britain by Scotprint Limited, Musselburgh

The Publisher's policy is to use paper manufactured from sustainable forests.

Contents

Good laboratory practice

 Danger

 Biohazard

 Flammable

 Corrosive

 Harmful or Irritant

 Toxic

 Wear eye protection

 Explosive

These are the safety symbols used in these books. You should get to know these so that you can recognise hazards that you might come across during your science lessons.

To avoid accidents you should:

- take special care when you see one of these symbols.
- always read through **all** the instructions given before you start doing your experiments.
- check with your teacher if you are not sure about any of the instructions.
- always check with your teacher before beginning any experiment that you have designed yourself.
- always wear eye protection when you see the eye protection symbol or when your teacher tells you.
- always wash your hands thoroughly with soap and water after handling pond water, soil, microbes, plants and animals.
- always stand when you are handling liquids so that you can move out of the way quickly if you spill anything.
- if you do spill anything on the bench wipe it up with a damp cloth, being careful not to get it on your hands.
- if you spill anything on your skin wash it off immediately and thoroughly with water. If you spill anything on your clothes tell your teacher.
- if you get anything in your eyes tell your teacher immediately.

Preface

This book (formerly *Chemistry 11–13*) has been expanded to make it suitable for students in Key Stage 3 of a modern science course. Some new material has been added to conform with the requirements of the National Curriculum and to increase the amount of 'socioeconomic' material. A new chapter has been added covering the Periodic Table.

The book still concentrates on explaining ideas rather than presenting vast amounts of factual information. It does this in a straightforward way without the use of expensive gimmicks and we are sure that it will continue to appeal to those who find chemistry fun. We feel that this presentation of chemistry as a coherent whole, rather than a series of unanswered questions, will help pupils to work on their own and lead them to a greater understanding. To test this understanding, the previously large number of questions has been further expanded. The text should be particularly useful for those approaching science as an academic study and those needing to revise for examinations.

The approach to practical work is essentially the same as in the previous book. We still feel it is important not to break up the text with too many practical instructions but instructions for key experiments have been included. Suggestions for many other experiments can be found in the Teachers' Guide.

We would still like to record our thanks to Alec Porch who helped us greatly in preparing the original manuscript.

Finally we owe grateful thanks to John Lewis for his advice on the manuscript and especially for all his work on the Teachers' Guide. We are also grateful to members of the CLEAPSS and ASE organisations for ensuring that the text meets with the current safety recommendations.

We would be pleased to know of any errors which the book contains and we would be grateful for suggestions as to how it can be further improved.

F. O. Harriss
H. J. C. Ferguson
Malvern 1991

Chapter 1

The separation and purification of solids

1.1 Introduction

Life today depends on industry and modern industry requires raw materials. These are rarely found in pure form. Substances which occur naturally are usually **mixtures** of chemicals: the air is a mixture, the sea is a mixture, rocks are often mixtures. Even a human being is a very complicated mixture of chemical substances. It is the task of the chemist to purify substances for use in industry and elsewhere.

Many chemicals do not occur naturally and have to be made from other substances which we do possess. This, too, is the chemist's job. A chemist needs pure substances to carry out experiments. The purification of substances is thus an important part of chemistry. This chapter describes some of the simple methods which can be used to purify chemicals.

1.2 Water, ice and steam

Before we can talk about purification, we must consider the three states in which substances are found. We will take water as an example.

If we cool water it **freezes** when a temperature of zero degrees centigrade (0 °C) is reached. It becomes 'solid water' which we call **ice**. When water is heated it boils when the temperature reaches 100 °C and turns into **steam**. This process is known as **evaporation**. So we know that water exists in three states: solid, liquid and gas. This is summarized in Fig 1.1. You will see that the opposite of freezing is **melting**. The opposite of evaporation is **condensation** (that is, cooling a gas until it becomes a liquid).

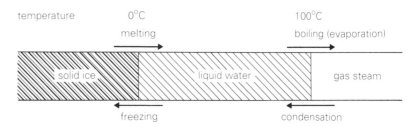

Fig 1.1.

Other substances also exist in the three states: solid, liquid and gas. However, the temperatures at which they melt and boil are different from those of water (see Section 3.2).

Fig 1.2 Saltworks in Cheshire.

1.3 The purification of rock salt

One of the commonest chemicals is salt (in chemical language, sodium chloride). This occurs in vast quantities in sea water. It has also been deposited on land as a result of the evaporation of the water from seas which existed millions of years ago. Rock salt is the name given to dirty brown salt crystals which are obviously impure. It is dug out of salt mines like those in Cheshire. It can be purified in a simple experiment.

Experiment 1.1
Purification of rock salt

1 Assemble the apparatus for the experiment (Fig 1.3).

2 Take a small amount of rock salt (Fig 1.4a) and grind up the crystals using a pestle and mortar (Fig 1.4b).

3 Place a beaker of water on a gauze on a tripod and use a Bunsen burner to heat the water until it is warm. Pour the crushed crystals into the water and stir them until they dissolve (Fig 1.4c). The solid brown dirt will not dissolve.

Safety note

For this experiment and all those following, safety glasses or goggles should be worn. This symbol will remind you.

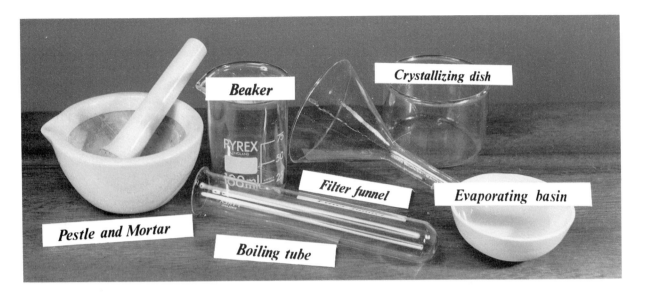

Fig 1.3 Apparatus for the purification of rock salt.

 **Safety note**

Stop before it has all evaporated, otherwise hot salt will spit out.

Fig 1.4 The purification of rock salt.

4 Fold a piece of filter paper and put it in a filter funnel, then support the funnel above an evaporating basin. Pour the mixture through the filter (Fig 1.4d). The brown dirt will remain on the paper, while the salt water will pass through it into the basin. This process is called filtration.

5 Heat the basin of salt water until crystals begin to form at the edges. Then continue the evaporation slowly using a small Bunsen flame (Fig 1.4e). Cubic crystals of salt will form. Before the evaporation is complete, filter the contents of the basin.

6 Wash the salt crystals with a little cold water and dry them with coarse filter paper or blotting paper (Fig 1.4f). They are now pure salt.

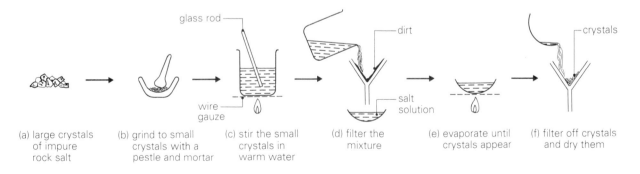

(a) large crystals of impure rock salt

(b) grind to small crystals with a pestle and mortar

(c) stir the small crystals in warm water

(d) filter the mixture

(e) evaporate until crystals appear

(f) filter off crystals and dry them

 **Safety note**

You should never taste anything in a science laboratory.

Dissolving

When salt dissolves in water, the solution formed appears to be very similar to water itself and it seems as if the salt has disappeared. However, we know that this is *not* so for several reasons:

1 The solution tastes salty.

2 We can get the salt back again by evaporation.

3 If we try to freeze the solution we find that it does not freeze at 0 °C, but several degrees lower. The addition of salt to water has lowered the freezing point. This is why salt is sprinkled on icy roads in winter.

4 The solution boils at a temperature higher than 100 °C (the boiling point of pure water).

The salt has **dissolved** in the water to form a **solution**. The solution is a mixture of the solid and water: the salt is known as the **solute** and the water as the **solvent**. The salt is **soluble** in the water whereas the brown dirt is insoluble. The large salt crystals have been split up into very small, invisible particles which have spread out through the water to form the solution.

Fig 1.5 Salt and rock salt crystals. The cubic, regular crystals are salt crystals.

If an **insoluble** substance is shaken with water a **suspension** results. You must be careful to distinguish between solutions, which are clear (transparent), and suspensions, which are cloudy until the visible particles have had time to settle. Many medicines and lotions are suspensions. Calamine lotion is an example. After a while, the white solid sinks to the bottom, leaving a clear solution above it. We are instructed to 'shake the bottle' to make a suspension before we use the lotion.

Filtration

In solutions, the water particles and the dissolved particles are very small and pass through a filter paper. However, the particles of solid in a suspension are larger and are trapped on the filter paper. This solid is called the **residue** while the clear liquid which comes through the filter is called the **filtrate**. Thus, in the purification of rock salt, the residue is the brown dirt and the filtrate is the salt solution.

As an alternative to filtration a machine called a centrifuge can be used. The test-tube is spun very fast and the solid goes to the bottom of the tube. The liquid can then be poured off.

Evaporation and crystallization

To separate solid salt from its solution, the solution can be heated. The water turns into steam, but the salt is unaffected. The water evaporates (turns from liquid into gas) and the solution becomes more **concentrated**.

There is a limit to the amount of salt which can be dissolved in a given quantity of water. A solution in which no more salt will dissolve is said to be **saturated** with salt. When enough water has evaporated from a salt solution, a saturated solution forms. As more water evaporates the salt starts to **crystallize** since there is no longer enough water to dissolve all the salt. Crystallization is often carried out in a crystallizing dish (Fig 1.3).

Once the crystals have been formed, they are separated from the remaining solution by filtration to stop any soluble impurities crystallizing. The crystals are then washed with water (to wash off any dissolved impurities) and dried.

Crystals

Many solids are much more soluble in hot solvents than in cold solvents. An example is a white solid called alum. When a hot solution of alum in water cools, crystals start to form. This is because the solid is less soluble in cold water than it is in hot water, so some of it comes out of solution. Common salt is slightly exceptional in that its solubility in water does not alter much with temperature and so it is necessary to get rid of some of the water (by evaporation) to allow salt crystals to form.

The size of crystals can be adjusted by cooling the solution at different rates. Slow cooling produces one or two large crystals, while fast cooling gives many very small crystals. This can be seen in experiments using copper sulphate or potassium nitrate. Larger crystals of salt can be grown by allowing the water to evaporate slowly at room temperature rather than by boiling off the water, but this takes a long time.

A really large crystal of copper sulphate can be grown by taking a small crystal of copper sulphate and suspending it in a saturated solution of copper sulphate (a solution which contains as much copper sulphate as possible) and allowing the water to evaporate slowly. This process can be repeated as the crystal becomes bigger.

Crystals have many different shapes (see Fig 1.6 overleaf for examples), and substancs therefore tend to crystallize separately. An exception to this is the alums which all crystallize as octahedra

Fig 1.6

(double square pyramids). If a purple chrome alum crystal is suspended in a colourless saturated solution of potash alum, it will gain a colourless layer.

a Copper sulphate crystals

b chromium (III) potassium sulphate crystals

c magnesium sulphate crystals X 40.

Crystals also form when substances freeze; such crystals tend to form quickly and can be studied under a low power microscope. Salol (phenyl salicylate) crystallizes well and you may also have seen the crystalline forms of water in snow flakes.

Question
Given a supply of very small crystals of iron alum (which is fairly soluble in cold water and very soluble in hot water), how would you attempt to grow a large crystal of iron alum?
For further reading on crystals see *Physics 11–14* Chapter 2.

1.4 The purification of other solids

Many solids are soluble in water and can be purified by using the method described in Section 1.2. For example, alum crystals can be purified in the same way as salt. The crystals can be obtained by allowing a hot saturated solution to cool slowly. Alum is much more soluble in hot water than in cold water; so a lot of crystals form as the solution cools.

However, some solids are insoluble in water. For example, the compound salol. So instead of water we use a different

Safety note

Propanone is highly flammable. Extinguish all flames before starting work.

Safety note

Trichloroethane is a harmful substance. You must avoid breathing its' vapour or getting it on your skin.

Safety note

Tetrachloromethane is toxic (more poisonous than chemicals marked harmful). Teachers only should do this experiment, and it must be done using a fume cupboard.

Fig 1.7 Finding melting points – two methods.

solvent in which salol does dissolve. Examples are propanone (acetone), trichloroethane and tetrachloromethane (carbon tetrachloride). Great care must be taken as these are often flammable (catch fire easily) or poisonous. The signs in the margin are used to show these hazards. To purify a solid, a solvent must be found which dissolves the pure substance but does not dissolve the impurities. The solid is dissolved in the solvent, the mixture is filtered and the solvent is evaporated: just as we did when purifying salt, using water as the solvent.

When a solid has been purified, its purity can be proved by finding its **melting point**. Two simple apparatuses for doing this are shown in Fig 1.7. In Fig 1.7a the substance is placed in a test-tube which is gently heated until the solid begins to melt. In Fig 1.7b the solid is ground up and a few very small crystals are placed on the aluminium block which is heated gently so that the temperature rises slowly. If all the crystals suddenly melt at a certain temperature which is known to be the melting point of the substance (for example 0°C for water, 43°C for salol), then the substance is pure. But if melting occurs over a range of temperatures *below* the known melting point, the substance is impure and the purification process must be repeated.

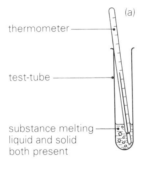

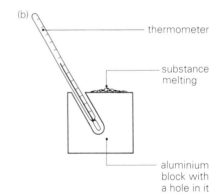

(a)
thermometer
test-tube
substance melting liquid and solid both present

(b)
thermometer
substance melting
aluminium block with a hole in it

Background Reading

Dry cleaning

The solvent which is used for most cleaning purposes is water. Not only has this the advantage of being cheap but it can also dissolve more substances than any other solvent. It is used to wash clothes, dishes and people. The washing process can usually be made more efficient if a small amount of a soap or a detergent is added. This aids the removal of grease which is insoluble in pure water.

Some objects would be damaged by the use of water to clean them, for example, parts of engines and certain articles of clothing, such as jackets. In these cases dry cleaning is used which involves the use of a solvent other than water. For clothing trichloroethane ('tri-chloro-ethane') (harmful) is used. This has the advantage that it is nonflammable (does not catch fire) and its vapour is not poisonous in small quantities. It dissolves the grease which has absorbed dirt and thus the dirt is freed from the fabric. After use the remaining solvent evaporates leaving the clothing clean.

Questions

1 Name a substance which might be present in dirty clothes and which is soluble in water.

2 Why might:
   a parts of engines,
   b jackets
   be damaged by washing with water?

3 Why is it important that a dry cleaning solvent is nonflammable and not poisonous?

4 Name another solvent which could be used for dry cleaning. Is it as suitable as trichloroethane (harmful)?

1.5 Chromatography

Some solids can be separated and purified by a method known as **chromatography**. Grass, for example, contains a number of pigments which are insoluble in water but which dissolve in other solvents such as propanone (acetone).

Experiment 1.2 Chromatography

1 Carefully crush some fresh grass in a pestle and mortar with about 5 cm^3 of propanone.

2 a Place a clean filter paper over an evaporating basin (Fig 1.8a).
   b Cut a 'tongue' in a second filter paper (Fig 1.8b) and place it over a beaker as shown.
   c Cut a small rectangular piece of filter paper into a small beaker (Fig 1.8c).

3 a Take one drop of the green solution from the mortar and place it in the centre of the filter paper (Fig 1.8a) and add a drop of propanone.
   b Put just enough propanone in the beaker to reach the tip of the paper 'tongue' (Fig 1.8b) and place a drop of the green solution in the centre of the filter paper.
   c Put propanone (1 cm deep) in the beaker (Fig 1.8c), then put a drop of the green solution 2 cm from the bottom of the paper and stand the paper in the solvent.

Safety note

Propanone is highly flammable. There must be no naked flames in the laboratory during this experiment.

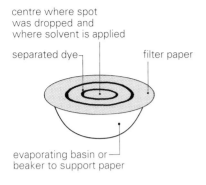

(a) Horizontal

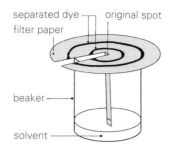

(b) Horizontal with tongue

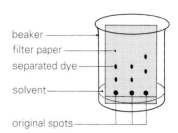

(c) Vertical

Fig 1.8 Chromatography.

4 Record what you see and draw the final appearance of each filter paper.

5 Try the same experiment with other solutions (e.g. ink) and with different solvents (e.g. water).

In the case of grass, the yellow xanthophyll travels furthest, followed by the green chlorophyll and finally the orange carotene. The separation can be improved if solvents other than propanone are used.

Separation occurs for two reasons. If several dyes are put into a particular solvent, some of them will dissolve more than others; the better they dissolve, the further they travel on the paper. Also the paper absorbs different dyes to different extents. So there is a 'tug of war' between the paper (trying to hold the dye at the starting point) and the solvent (trying to pull the dye along with it). This 'tug of war' decides how far the dye will move relative to the distance travelled by the solvent.

After chromatography has taken place the piece of paper is known as a **chromatogram**. Chromatograms can be used to discover which dyes a particular mixture contains. Fig 1.9 gives an example of a chromatogram which could be used to investigate three orange dyes. Spots of three orange dyes, C, D and E, are placed on the start line and also spots of a red dye, A, and a

Fig 1.9 A chromatogram.

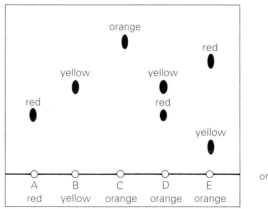

yellow dye, B, which might be present in the orange dyes. The chromatogram is then placed in a large beaker with a layer of solvent at the bottom (Fig 1.8c). The solvent rises up the paper and the dyes follow to varying extents. When the solvent has reached the top of the paper, the spots of dyes have reached the positions shown in Fig 1.9.

The results show that the orange dye, D, is a mixture of two dyes, one red the other yellow, since it separates into two spots. The red dye is A, as the red dye spot and A have risen to the same height; the yellow dye is B for similar reasons. Dye C gives only one spot and is probably a pure orange dye rather than a mixture of yellow and red. E is a mixture, but the red dye is not the same as A because the spot does not rise to the same height; nor is the yellow dye B.

Chromatography is also suitable for investigating coloured inks, when water can sometimes be used as the solvent. Inks in felt-tip pens often contain several dyes.

Chromatography is not suitable for separating large quantities of dyes and so other methods must be used instead. One method is fractional distillation which is described in the next chapter.

Background Reading

Practical uses of chromatography

Chromatography is a very valuable tool for finding out which dyes are present in a mixture. It can be used when only very small samples are available.

Food analysts needs to know if illegal colours have been used in food. They run chromatograms of the colours from food alongside spots of illegal dyes. If the spots rise to the same heights it is likely that illegal dyes have been used.

Picture restorers need to know which pigments have been used in an ancient painting. They can do this by running a chromatogram. On this they would place tiny spots of a paint from the picture. They would also put on small spots of various likely pigments. Spots which rise to the same height on the chromatogram show which pigments are present in the paint.

Chromatography can also be used to separate colourless substances. The final chromatogram is sprayed with a chemical which makes the spots show up. In this way doctors can examine blood. They can find out whether substances are present which can cause illness.

Forensic scientists are employed by the police in the fight against crime. They can use chromatography, for example, to show that the oil from a car is the same as some oil found at the scene of a crime.

Question
Write an imaginative story about solving a problem using chromatography. Imagine you are a picture restorer, a food analyst, a doctor or a forensic scientist.

Summary

1 Substances exist in three states: solid, liquid and gas.

2 Many impure solids can be purified by dissolving them in water and filtering to remove insoluble impurities. The solution is then evaporated or allowed to crystallize. Sometimes other solvents are used instead of water.

3 A pure substance melts at one temperature. An impure substance melts over a range of temperatures.

4 Chromatography can be used to separate mixtures of coloured substances.

Questions

1 Your father has spilt sugar into some savoury rice. Explain to him how he could try to obtain the rice again. Why would this method not be suitable for a mixture of salt and sugar?

2 Coffee can be made by pouring hot water through a filter containing ground coffee. The coffee drips into the jug below.
  a Why is hot water used?
  b Why is a filter used?
  c Why is it not necessary to do this when you make instant coffee?

3 When salt is purified, explain why:
  a The impure salt is crushed.
  b The impure solution is filtered.
  c The solution is heated after it has been filtered.

4 a You wish to make a concentrated solution of lump rock salt in water as quickly as possible. State three things you do to hasten the process.
  b Explain simply why any one of them is effective.

5 When a boy was asked to find out whether chalk was soluble in water, he added water to some chalk, filtered the mixture and transferred one drop of the clear liquid to a microscope slide. After evaporation of water a trace of white solid remained on the slide.
  a What can he deduce from this experiment?
  b What was the reason for filtering the mixture?

6 a When fructose, a sweet compound derived from certain fruits, is added to water at room temperature, it seems to disappear. A possible explanation for this is: the fructose . . . in the water. Choose the word from this list which would fill the gap:

condenses, crystallizes, dissolves, evaporates, melts.

b In an attempt to find out whether stirring increased the rate of disappearance of the fructose in the water, equal masses of fructose were put in separate containers with equal volumes of water and stirred at different rates. The times for the complete disappearance of the fructose were as given below:

Rate of stirring (rev per minute)   0   5   10
Time of disappearance (minutes)   10   6   2

Did increasing the rate of stirring increase, decrease or have no effect on the rate of disappearance of the fructose?

c Why was it considered necessary to keep the masses of fructose and the volumes of water the same in all three experiments?

d Write a brief set of instructions for a method of finding out whether or not the rate of disappearance depends on the temperature of the mixture.

7 Benzoic acid is a white solid which is insoluble in cold water, but soluble in hot water. Charcoal is insoluble in water.

a Explain the steps by which you would obtain pure benzoic acid from a mixture of benzoic acid and charcoal.

b How would you show that the benzoic acid crystals were pure?

c Salt is soluble in cold water. How would you obtain pure benzoic acid from a mixture of benzoic acid, charcoal and salt?

8 Sand is insoluble in water and insoluble in tetrachloromethane. Common salt is soluble in water, but insoluble in tetrachloromethane. Wax is insoluble in water, but soluble in tetrachloromethane. A scientist is given a mixture of sand, common salt and wax. How would she obtain a pure sample of each of them?

9 Salol melts at 43°C and becomes liquid salol.
Liquid salol and a solution of salol are both colourless liquids.

a What is the difference between liquid salol and a solution of salol?

b How would you obtain salol crystals from a solution of salol?

c How would you obtain solid salol from liquid salol?

10 Tincture of iodine is a disinfectant, and is made by dissolving crystals of iodine in dilute alcohol. Name:

a The solvent.   **b** The solute.   **c** The solution.

11
	Solvent **A**	Solvent **B**
substance **X**	soluble	insoluble
substance **Y**	insoluble	soluble

Suggest names for the solvents A and B and the substances X and Y.

12 A blackcurrant-flavoured ice-lolly is coloured purple. Write the instructions for an experiment to find out whether it contained a purple food colouring or a mixture of a red and a blue one.

13 **a** The extract from a beech leaf is said to contain a number of compounds which are coloured differently. How would you test this statement?

b You are given a sample of salol, a white solid that melts easily. What experiment would you carry out in order to test whether it is pure?

14 The chromatogram in Fig 1.10 was obtained using a set of felt-tip pens with water as the solvent.

Fig 1.10.

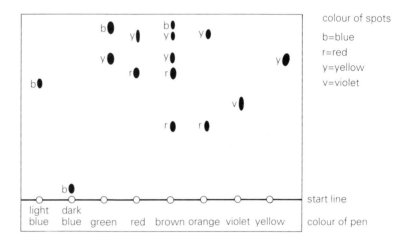

a Which pens contained only one dye?

b Green can be obtained by mixing blue and yellow. Has the manufacturer done this? Has he used the light blue, the dark blue or a different blue altogether? Give your reasons.

c Brown can be obtained by mixing red and green. What did the manufacturer do?

d Is the yellow used in the orange pen the same one that is used in the green pen? How many different yellows have been used in the eight pens?

e Which of the dyes is likely to be the least soluble in water?

f This experiment was carried out at home in the holidays. Explain how you would obtain such a chromatogram using only materials that can be found in the home.

Chapter 2

Separation and purification of liquids

2.1 Immiscible liquids

Just as some solids are insoluble in some solvents, so some liquids mix together and some do not. Those that do not mix are said to be **immiscible**. Water is immiscible with many liquids such as paraffin and tetrachloromethane.

The separation of immiscible liquids is very simple. The mixture is placed in a separating funnel (Fig 2.1) where the less dense one will form the upper layer. The two liquids can be run out of the funnel one after the other, after the bung is removed.

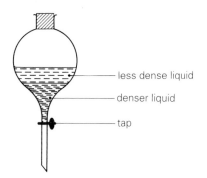

less dense liquid

denser liquid

tap

Fig 2.1 A separating funnel.

2.2 Distillation

If the liquids mix (for example water and ethanol) or if we have a solution of a solid in a liquid, the problem is more difficult and we have to use distillation. Consider first how to obtain a pure liquid from a solution of a solid in the liquid. If the solution is evaporated, only the liquid boils off and the solid remains behind (Section 1.3). If the vapour[*] is condensed (turned back to a liquid) we shall have achieved our aim. The process of evaporation followed by condensation is called **distillation**.

Experiment 2.1
Simple distillation

some vapour condenses

some vapour does not condense

beaker

liquid turning to vapour

antibumping granules

condensed liquid

Fig 2.2 Simple distillation.

1 Place about 3 cm of copper sulphate solution in a test-tube with a few **antibumping granules**. These are added to prevent violent boiling which is known as **bumping**.

2 Connect up the apparatus as shown in Fig 2.2, standing the empty test-tube in an empty beaker.

3 Heat the copper sulphate solution gently with a Bunsen burner.

4 Some water will collect in the empty test-tube: some will also escape as steam.

[*] The word vapour is often used to refer to a gas which can easily be condensed back to a liquid.

5 Add cold water to the empty beaker supporting the collecting test-tube.

6 This cools the test-tube and more water condenses.

A more efficient piece of apparatus is the Liebig condenser which uses a continuous stream of cold water flowing in an outer jacket (Fig 2.3). The water should enter this at the bottom so that the jacket is always full. Then a slow rate of flow can be used.

Fig 2.3 Distillation using a Liebig condenser.

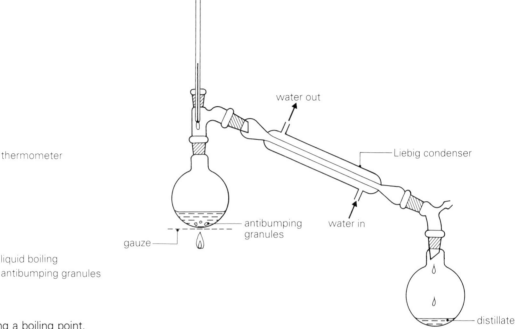

Fig 2.4 Measuring a boiling point.

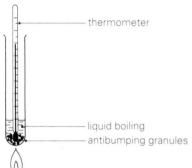

Safety note

Be careful with flammable liquids.

If copper sulphate solution or ink are distilled, the liquid which condenses (the distillate) is colourless and we presume it is pure water. This can be tested by measuring its boiling point using the apparatus shown in Fig 2.4. The temperature of the water rises as it is heated and then remains steady–this is the boiling point. Water boils at about 100 °C (the exact temperature depends on the atmospheric pressure). If the boiling temperature increases during the distillation then the distillate is a mixture of liquids rather than one pure liquid. Great care must be taken when distilling liquids other than water since they are often flammable (catch fire easily).

2.3 Fractional distillation

What do you think would happen if a mixture of ethanol (highly flammable) (b.p. 79 °C) and water (b.p. 100 °C) (two miscible liquids) were distilled in the apparatus of Fig 2.3? Quite a reasonable answer might be that the ethanol, having a lower boiling point, would boil off first, leaving the water. However this does not happen; the distillate consists of a mixture of ethanol and water, but it has a slightly higher proportion of ethanol than the original mixture. If this distillate were distilled, the new distillate would be richer in ethanol. This process could be repeated, but it is a very laborious way of separating the mixture.

However, in the apparatus shown in Fig 2.5, this process of continual distillation does occur. The mixture of ethanol and water vapours rises to a certain point and condenses. The liquid drops down a little. There the temperature is hotter, so it boils again. The vapour rises, but it condenses not far above the place where it condensed before. Thus in the column a very large number of 'evaporation then condensation' steps occur. Each time the vapour gets a little richer in ethanol. So, if the column is big enough, almost pure ethanol vapour comes out at the top. (Ethanol and water cannot be separated completely by distillation). The column is called a **fractionating column** because it divides mixtures of liquids into parts or fractions according to their boiling point. This process is called **fractional distillation**.

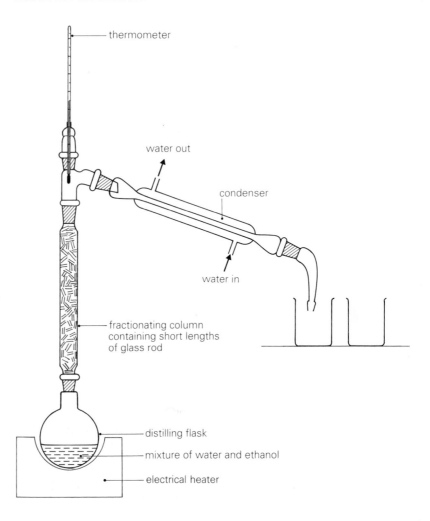

Fig 2.5 Fractional distillation of a mixture of water and ethanol.

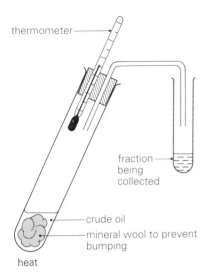

thermometer

fraction being collected

crude oil

mineral wool to prevent bumping

heat

Fig 2.6 Simple laboratory distillation of crude oil.

The initial step in the refining of petroleum (crude oil) is fractional distillation. Because crude oil contains hundreds of compounds, pure liquids are not produced; instead 'fractions' are obtained. In each fraction are all the compounds which boil within a certain temperature range. In the laboratory experiment (Fig 2.6) the test-tube itself acts as the fractionating column.

Gentle heating of the crude oil in a water bath gives the first fraction, boiling between room temperature and about 70 °C. It is very **volatile** (turns easily to a gas), very flammable and can be poured easily. As heating continues (above 100 °C, heat with a flame) other fractions may be collected, until the last (boiling above about 180 °C) is involatile, cannot be burnt and is very **viscous** (treacly). In addition it is usually darker in colour. The fractions are not pure substances: this can be seen from the fact that the temperature rises as a particular sample is being collected. The fractions are still mixtures of compounds, but each fraction contains a group of substances with similar boiling points. Thus the fractions behave differently from one another.

2.4 Industrial distillation of oil

Petroleum is separated into its different fractions using a fractionating tower (Figs 2.7 and 2.8). The most volatile components go to the top of the tower. At each level it becomes cooler and some of the compounds in oil condense. The remainder continue to rise, as gases, to higher levels. The liquid at each level can fall to a lower level; the temperature is higher there and so the volatile compounds will again turn into gases.

Fig 2.7 A fractional distillation unit.

Fig 2.8 The industrial distillation of crude oil.

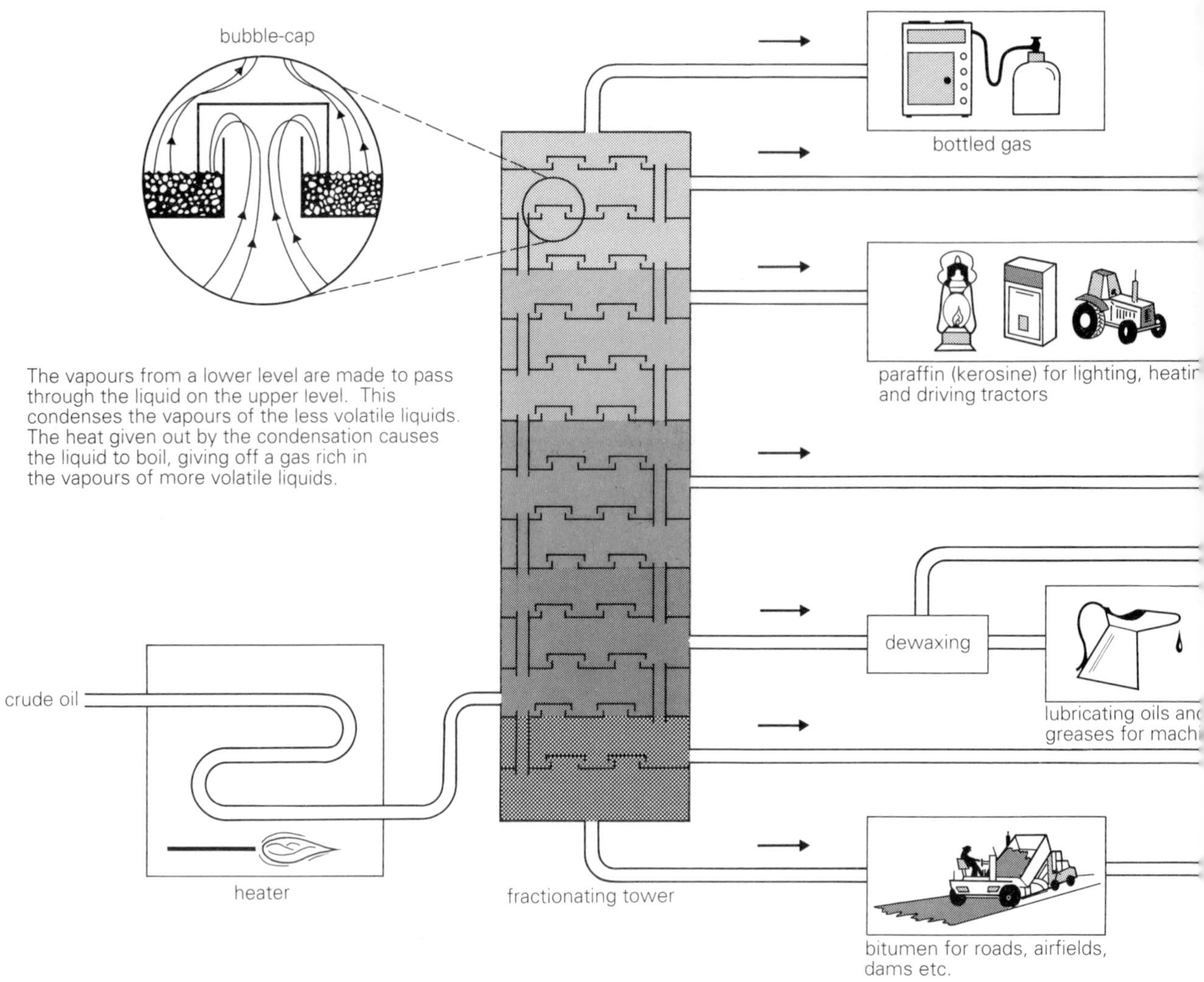

chief uses of oil products

bubble-cap

The vapours from a lower level are made to pass
through the liquid on the upper level. This
condenses the vapours of the less volatile liquids.
The heat given out by the condensation causes
the liquid to boil, giving off a gas rich in
the vapours of more volatile liquids.

crude oil

heater

fractionating tower

bottled gas

paraffin (kerosine) for lighting, heatin
and driving tractors

dewaxing

lubricating oils and
greases for mach

bitumen for roads, airfields,
dams etc.

Distillation is only the first process in the refining of petroleum
and further processes are used to obtain the products we need.
Fuel for motor cars comes from the gasoline fraction and jet
aeroplane fuel comes from the kerosene fraction. The heavy oils
are used to make fuel oil for ships and bitumen for roads, though
a further process, known as cracking, can break down these
heavy oils to produce gasoline and the raw materials for plastics.

2.5 Distillation of air

Air is a mixture of gases and these can be separated by cooling
air until it condenses, then fractionally distilling the resulting liquid air.
Carbon dioxide and water vapour are removed first.

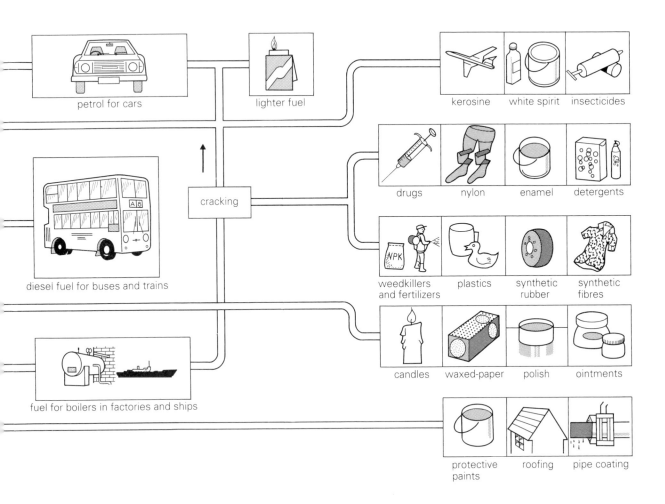

examples of other uses

petrol for cars

lighter fuel

kerosine   white spirit   insecticides

diesel fuel for buses and trains

cracking

drugs   nylon   enamel   detergents

weedkillers   plastics   synthetic   synthetic
and fertilizers   rubber   fibres

fuel for boilers in factories and ships

candles   waxed-paper   polish   ointments

protective   roofing   pipe coating
paints

The method of condensation relies on the fact that gases cool when allowed to expand suddenly. You may have noticed this when making soda water with carbon dioxide. The opposite effect is that air tends to warm up when compressed and you may have felt this happening when pumping up bicycle tyres.

Air is compressed, cooled and then allowed to expand suddenly so that it gets very cold and becomes liquid. If the liquid is allowed to warm up in a fractionating column the various gases can be separated, though there are difficulties because the boiling points of the substances are so close to each other. The composition of the air is given in Chapter 4.

Summary

1 Immiscible liquids can be separated using a separating funnel.

2 The solvent can be separated from a solution by distillation, which involves evaporation and condensation.

3 Mixtures of liquids can be separated by fractional distillation using a fractionating column.

4 Fractional distillation is used in industry to separate crude oil and liquid air into their components.

Background Reading

Using distillation to make alcoholic drinks (spirits)

Starch or sugar can be turned into ethanol (alcohol) (highly flammable) by a process called **fermentation.** This is carried out by the micro-organism yeast. When barley is fermented, beer is formed. Fermented grapes give wine. However an ethanol concentration of over 15% cannot be obtained by fermentation, as this ethanol level 'kills' the yeast. In order to make drinks with a higher ethanol content, the liquids made by fermentation are **distilled** . The drinks which result from distillation are called spirits.

Fig 2.9 A whisky still.

The distillation of a mixture of ethanol and water is discussed in Section 2.3. If the correct conditions are used an ethanol-water mixture containing a high proportion of ethanol can be produced. (This is illegal without an excise licence.) The solution also contains the other volatile materials present in the original liquids which give the characteristic taste. In the case of whisky, the drink is then diluted with water to about 40 % ethanol, and colouring matter is added. Different countries have produced different spirits. All have been responsible for alcoholism though they give pleasure to those who sample them in moderation.

Country	Drink	Made from
Scotland	whisky	barley
France	brandy	wine (grapes)
Holland	gin	corn (flavoured with juniper)
West Indies	rum	molasses (sugar cane)
Scandinavia	snaps	potatoes
Russia	vodka	corn or potatoes

Liqueurs are spirits to which other flavours have been added. A mixture of wine and brandy is known as a fortified wine; examples are sherry and port.

Question
What is meant by 'other volatile materials present in the original liquids'?

Questions

1 Give the names of the processes which you would use to separate the following substances from the following mixtures:
  a Sand from a suspension of sand in salt solution.
  b Water from copper sulphate solution.
  c A red dye from a mixture of red, blue and yellow dyes.

2 a Give an example of a solvent which contains no water.
  b Give an example of a solute that dissolves in this solvent.
  c What is the name given to the process by which you could recover a solvent from a solution?

3 You and a friend decide to produce some drinking water from a bucket of dirty sea water.
  a Your friend says he can easily get the bits of seaweed and dirt out. What does he do?
  b You say you can remove the salt. What do you do with the clean sea water to make it tasteless? (Draw a diagram of the apparatus you would use.)
  c Your friend claims that sea salt is better for you than ordinary salt. How would you obtain a sample of dry sea salt crystals from your sea water?

4 Royal blue ink can be distilled to produce a colourless liquid which boils at 100 °C.

a Draw a diagram of simple apparatus that could be used in this experiment.

b A Liebig condenser can be used to make the distillation more efficient. Draw a diagram of such a condenser and explain how it works.

c What is the distillate (the colourless liquid that boils at 100 °C)?

d What has happened to the dyes in the ink?

e What experiment would you do to find out how many dyes there are in the ink?

5 How would you obtain:

a Sand from gritty sea water?

b Salt from sea water?

c Pure water from sea water?

d Water from a mixture of petrol and water? (Petrol does not dissolve in water.)

e Petrol from a mixture of petrol and water?

f The colours in a copper beech leaf?

6 Universal indicator consists of a number of dyes dissolved in ethanol.

a How would you try to separate the dyes?

b How would you obtain ethanol from universal indicator?

c How would you show that the liquid you obtained was ethanol?

7 In an essay on petroleum a boy wrote: 'Crude oil can be distilled into many different fractions, with the lighter, more volatile fractions coming off first.'

Explain briefly the meaning of the following words:

a Crude.

b Distilled.

c Volatile.

8 This is an extract from an article entitled 'The Holy Water of Ireland' from *The Daily Telegraph Colour Supplement*, 14 August 1970. Read it carefully and answer the questions below.

Inside the barn the first of two stills was being set up on bits of breeze block, leaving a space for the gas ring underneath. First, next to the door was the steel drum into which the wash was poured, a bucket at a time, from the barrels outside. In the top of the oil drum a neat circular hole held the still-head, a bottomless wooden bucket with its top covered over. From a hole in the side of the still-head the conical arm sloped gradually down to the cooling barrel where it joined the head of the five-bend 'worm'. The copper worm disappeared beneath the surface of the cool brown spring water in the wooden barrel to emerge from a small hole at the bottom...

The stills were now ready and the gas cylinders were brought in and connected, a bright blue flame roaring up beneath the two oil drums. There was little to do now but watch and wait till the first run, the 'singlings' started to come over. Seamus adjusted the heat* carefully so that it would bring off the alcohol and leave the water behind...We sat and watched until a brown liquid started to trickle from the end of the first worm. Seamus bent and tasted it with his finger. The heat* was too great and it was not coming off strong enough. He lowered the gas and threw a couple of buckets of water over the side of the drum to cool it a little...

He tasted it again. 'That's it, the singlings', he said, and put a bucket beneath to catch the impure whiskey.

* The writer means temperature

a This process could obviously be carried out in laboratory apparatus. Give the names of the pieces of equipment which would correspond to:
   (i) The steel drum (line 3).
   (ii) The worm and cooling barrel (lines 9 and 10).
b Draw a diagram of the still described above as you imagine it might look.
c How would you explain to Seamus, in simple terms:
   (i) Why lowering the temperature produced more alcohol in the singlings.
   (ii) Why he might have to change the water in the cooling barrel occasionally.
d What do you think the 'wash' might have been made from?
e Before the very strong 'worm beer' is produced, which is diluted to make the final whiskey, another distillation is carried out. Why do you think this is?

9 a Draw a diagram of an apparatus suitable for distilling a small quantity of crude oil in the laboratory, so as to separate it into about four fractions. Label your diagram.
b There would be a risk of fire in distilling a fairly large bulk of crude oil in the laboratory. Mention one way in which this risk could be minimized.
c How does the first fraction differ from the last fraction in:
   (i) Colour?
   (ii) Flammability?
   (iii) Viscosity?
d Why would the last fraction be unsuitable as fuel for a motor car? What properties does motor car fuel have?
e Give one reason for believing that each of the four fractions is a mixture rather than a pure substance.

10 a Where in an oil refinery would you find a 'bubble-cap'? How does a bubble-cap work?

   b A volatile substance in crude oil enters a fractionating tower. Why does it rise to the top?

   c An involatile substance in crude oil enters the tower. Why does it go to the bottom?

11 Use your library and reference books to help you to answer the following questions.

   a How do oil men set about looking for oil?

   b How do they test their theory that an oilfield exists in a certain place?

   c How do they get the oil to the surface?

   d How do they take the oil from the well to the refinery or nearest port?

Chapter 3   Heating substances

3.1 Reversible and irreversible changes

If some sugar is heated, it melts and then turns slowly brown and eventually black. The brown substance is known as caramel, and the caramel cannot be turned back into sugar again. The change is permanent and irreversible – such changes are considered later. First we shall consider changes which are **reversible**, where the product can easily be turned back into its original form.

3.2 Melting and boiling

(See also Section 1.2.)
When water is heated some of it evaporates; but most of it goes on getting hotter. However, when the temperature reaches the boiling point, it remains there while all the water evaporates, turning into steam. At the boiling point, both water and steam are present. If we continue heating, more water turns into steam; if we cool the steam then the process is reversed and steam turns into water again. This is known as condensation and is what happens in the second stage of distillation (Section 2.2).

If water is cooled, its temperature drops until the freezing point (0 °C) is reached. At this temperature both water and ice are present. If cooling continues, more water turns into ice (the temperature remains at 0 °C), but if the mixture is heated the process is reversed and ice turns back into water again. (0 °C can of course be referred to as the **melting point** of ice). Reversible processes can be represented by double arrows $\rightleftharpoons$ and the heating and cooling of water can be represented as:

$$\text{ice} \overset{0\,°C}{\rightleftharpoons} \text{water} \overset{100\,°C}{\rightleftharpoons} \text{steam}$$

Since ice, water and steam are chemically the same substance, in the three different **states of matter**, solid, liquid and gas, we can also represent the change like this:

$$\text{solid water} \overset{0\,°C}{\rightleftharpoons} \text{liquid water} \overset{100\,°C}{\rightleftharpoons} \text{gaseous water}$$

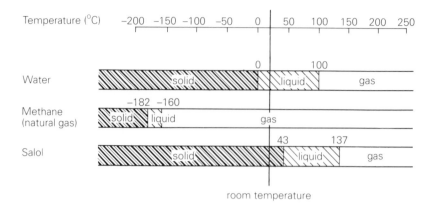

Fig 3.1 Melting and boiling points for three substances.

Almost every substance can exist in each of the three states — solid, liquid or gas — but the melting and boiling points are different for every substance. Some examples are given in Fig 3.1.

The state in which we find a substance depends on the temperature at which we examine it. For example, above 137 °C all three of the substances in Fig 3.1 would be gases and below −182 °C all would be solids. Normally of course we work at 'room temperature' which is about 20 °C. At this temperature water is a liquid, methane is a gas and salol is a solid.

3.3 Subliming

It is possible for ice to turn straight into a gas without melting. This often happens on cold, clear winter days. This process of a solid turning directly into a gas is known as **sublimation** and, as in melting and boiling, the change is reversible (Fig 3.2).

Ammonium chloride is a white solid which sublimes when heated and this fascinated the medieval alchemists who knew it as 'sal ammoniac'. Other substances which sublime are iodine (a purple solid) and 'dry ice' (solid white carbon dioxide which sublimes at − 78°C).

Safety note

Iodine vapour and solid are corrosive.

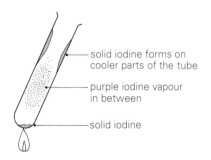

- solid iodine forms on cooler parts of the tube
- purple iodine vapour in between
- solid iodine

Fig 3.2 Sublimation.

3.4 Chemical changes

Changes of state such as melting, boiling and subliming are examples of **physical changes** in which the chemical nature of the substance does not alter. For example, water and steam are both the same chemical. Again, when wax melts, the liquid produced is still wax, only in a different form, and no new substance has been made.

Changes which result in new chemicals being formed are called **chemical reactions.** Some chemical reactions are reversible and examples are given in the next section.

3.5 Heating copper sulphate and cobalt chloride crystals

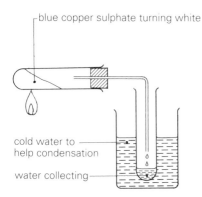

Safety note

Anhydrous copper sulphate is harmful. Wash it off your skin immediately.

blue copper sulphate turning white

cold water to help condensation

water collecting

Fig 3.3 Heating copper sulphate.

Experiment 3.1
Heating copper sulphate and testing for water

1 Quarter fill a test-tube with blue copper sulphate crystals.

2 Weigh the test-tube and crystals.

3 Set up the apparatus shown in Fig 3.3 and gently heat the test-tube.

4 The copper sulphate crystals turn white and a colourless liquid collects in the cooled test-tube.

5 When no more liquid is formed, allow the white solid and the heated test-tube to cool down and weigh them again.

6 If you have collected enough liquid, use the apparatus in Fig 2.4 to measure its boiling point. This will be 100 °C, showing that the liquid is water.

7 Add a drop of distilled water to the white solid when it has cooled. It turns blue again and the test-tube becomes warm or hot.

The mass of the white solid in the test-tube (step 5) is less than the mass of the blue crystals in the test-tube before heating. We say that the blue crystals have **decomposed**, that is, they have been broken down chemically.

When the white solid is cooled and water is added to it, the solid becomes warm and turns blue again. The process is reversible and can be written:

$$\text{hydrated copper sulphate} \underset{}{\overset{\text{heat}}{\rightleftharpoons}} \text{anhydrous copper sulphate} + \text{water}$$
$$\quad\quad\quad\text{blue} \quad\quad\quad\quad\quad\quad\quad\quad\quad\text{white}$$

The words **hydrated** and **anhydrous** are based on Greek and mean 'with water' and 'without water'.

Another compound which behaves like copper sulphate is cobalt chloride. The hydrated form consists of red crystals which, when heated, give off water and leave a dark blue solid, anhydrous cobalt chloride. The blue solid turns red again if water is added to it, and a pink-red solution forms on top of the solid. This is another example of a reversible decomposition.

$$\text{hydrated cobalt chloride} \underset{}{\overset{\text{heat}}{\rightleftharpoons}} \text{anhydrous cobalt chloride} + \text{water}$$
$$\quad\quad\text{red} \quad\quad\quad\quad\quad\quad\quad\quad\quad\quad\text{blue}$$

3.6 Testing for water

The colour changes described in the last section can be used to test for the presence of water. One such test involves the addition of anhydrous copper sulphate to a liquid thought to contain water. If the copper sulphate turns blue then water is *present* in the liquid. The test does not prove that the liquid is *pure* water. If only a very small drop of the liquid is available, cobalt chloride paper is used. This paper is pale pink to start with. When it is heated gently, water is driven off and the paper turns blue. This blue paper is placed in the liquid. If it turns pale pink again, the liquid contains water.

These tests show only that water is present, and a liquid which gives a positive result may be a mixture of water with some other substance (for example salt solution). To test whether a liquid is pure or is a solution the boiling point must be found. If it boils steadily at or near 100 °C[*] it is pure water. A solution of a solid in water will boil at a temperature *higher* than that of pure water. As the water evaporates and the solution becomes more concentrated, the boiling point will rise.

3.7 Permanent changes

So far we have looked at various changes which all had one thing in common: they were reversible. (These changes are sometimes called 'temporary'). In the rest of this chapter we are concerned with changes which cannot easily be reversed. These are known as **permanent** changes.

Before substances are heated they are weighed and after heating the residue which remains is weighed. There are three possibilities: a gain in mass, no change in mass, or a loss in mass. Where no difference of mass is recorded the substance has not changed chemically (but a physical change may have occurred, as for example when ice turns into water). If there is a gain in mass this is always due to the air, part of which has combined with the substance. Such changes are considered at the end of this chapter (Section 3.11) and in Chapter 4.

What happens when mass is lost? Has matter been destroyed? If we look into these situations more carefully we find that a gas has been given off, and we can show this by collecting it. It is not an easy job to weigh gases, but when this is done, it is found that the mass of the gas makes up for the mass lost by the substance which was heated:

$$\text{substance} \longrightarrow \text{solid residue} + \text{gas}$$
$$\text{mass } m \qquad\qquad \text{mass } (m - x) \qquad \text{mass } x$$

[*] The exact value depends on the atmospheric pressure.

When a substance is heated one gas which may be given off is steam, which can be easily condensed back to water. Section 3.5 dealt with the loss of water from two *hydrated* salts: copper sulphate and cobalt chloride. If all the water had been condensed and weighed, it would have just made up for the mass lost by the crystals when they were heated.

In these cases the loss of water was *reversible*, but not all compounds which lose water do so reversibly. For example, purple crystals of chrome alum lose water (which can be tested in the usual way) leaving a green solid. Addition of water to this green solid does not result in the purple crystals forming again. This is an example of a *permanent* change.

3.8 Loss of oxygen

If substances like potassium permanganate or red lead oxide are heated they lose mass. Any attempt to condense the gas (using the apparatus shown in Fig 3.3) would fail because the gas being given off is oxygen, not steam.

Experiment 3.2
Collecting oxygen over water

1 Part fill a tank with water.

2 Fill two or three test-tubes with water by immersing them in the tank. Keep them full until needed by standing them upside down in the tank with their mouths under water.

3 Place a small amount of potassium permanganate in a test-tube fitted with a bung and a delivery tube.

4 Place the open end of the delivery tube under water in the tank and hold one of the water-filled test-tubes over it (Fig 3.4).

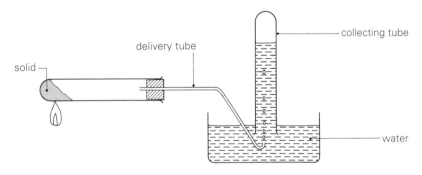

Safety note

Take care when heating potassium permanganate. It is harmful.

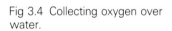
Fig 3.4 Collecting oxygen over water.

5 Heat the solid. The oxygen given off forces its way through the apparatus and fills the collecting tube by displacing the water.

6 Cork the gas-filled tubes under water so that they can be kept. The first tube will contain a mixture of air and oxygen because air is first pushed out of the apparatus by the oxygen.

Safety note

Beware of suck-back.

Fig 3.5 Measuring the volume
of gas given off when a solid
is heated.

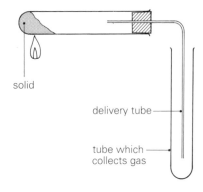

solid

delivery tube

tube which
collects gas

Fig 3.6 Collecting carbon dioxide
(denser than air).

lime water

Fig 3.7 Testing for carbon dioxide
(method 1).

7 When you have finished, remove the delivery tube from the water before you stop heating. Otherwise the air will cool and contract, sucking water back into the hot tube.

If the volume of oxygen is to be measured, a gas syringe may be used instead of a collecting tube (Fig 3.5). If no gas syringe is available, a graduated tube (marked with volume) may be used instead of the test-tube shown in Fig 3.4*.

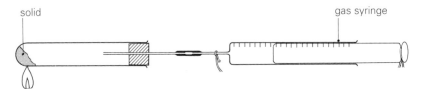

solid

gas syringe

The chemical test for oxygen is that it will 'rekindle a glowing splint'. A **splint** is a thin piece of wood. This is lit and blown out so that is glows; then, if it is placed in oxygen it catches fire again (rekindles). The gas in the collecting tubes may be tested in this way, or the glowing splint may be rekindled at the mouth of the tube in which the gas is being prepared. Sometimes the rekindling makes a slight noise, which should not be confused with the 'squeaky pop' in the test for hydrogen.

3.9 Loss of carbon dioxide

When some compounds, known as carbonates (for example copper carbonate) are heated, they give off a gas called carbon dioxide. (As it does this, copper carbonate turns from green to black.) The gas may be collected over water as in Fig 3.4, but this is not very satisfactory because some of the carbon dioxide dissolves in the water. As it is heavier (denser) than air it can be collected in the apparatus shown in Fig 3.6.

Experiment 3.3
Testing for carbon dioxide

1 Put some limewater (2 cm deep) in a test-tube.

2 Put a small amount of copper carbonate in a second test-tube and set up the apparatus shown in Fig 3.7.

Safety note

Copper carbonate is harmful.

* A more convenient laboratory preparation of oxygen is described in Section 5.4

(a) collect carbon dioxide
in a teat pipette

(b) bubble the gas
through lime water

Fig 3.8 Testing for carbon dioxide
(method 2).

3 Gently heat the copper carbonate and notice the colour change.

4 Bubbles of gas come out of the end of the glass tube and rise through the limewater. What do you observe?

5 Remove the tube from the water before you stop heating, in case of suck-back.

6 An alternative way of carrying out the test is shown in Fig 3.8. A teat pipette is placed in the gas to be tested (Fig 3.8a) and squeezed several times. The gas is then blown out through limewater (Fig 3.8b) which is watched for milkiness.

The limewater turns milky showing that the gas is carbon dioxide. Limewater is calcium hydroxide and the milkiness is a fine suspension of calcium carbonate. If a test-tube of carbon dioxide is to be tested, some limewater can simply be added and the test-tube shaken. It is important not to use too much limewater as the milkiness will take a long time to appear. Another problem can be that the milkiness disappears if too much carbon dioxide is present, but this is only a difficulty if the experiment is left and not watched.

3.10 Heating sulphur

When sulphur is heated in a crucible which is open to the air, a blue flame is seen and the solid disappears leaving no trace except for a sharp smell. Does this mean that the sulphur is decomposing like the substances described above? The question can be answered by heating sulphur in the absence of air. (This can be done by heating sulphur in a test-tube, the sulphur gas which is given off pushes the air out of the tube before the sulphur is hot enough to catch fire.) The sulphur melts, then turns into a thick, black substance and finally boils. It does not decompose and therefore the original disappearance of the sulphur had something to do with the air. In fact the sulphur has **reacted** with part of the air to form a gas, as we shall see in the next chapter.

3.11 Heating magnesium and copper

When a piece of magnesium ribbon is heated in air, it will eventually flare up and burn with a brilliant white flame. A white ash is left behind. If this reaction is carried out in a crucible (with a lid to stop the ash escaping), it is found that the ash weighs more than the magnesium did. Something has been taken from the air and has increased the mass of the magnesium, changing it into a new substance.

Another experiment is to fold up a piece of copper foil, hold it in tongs, and heat it in air. This reaction is much less spectacular than the heating of magnesium. The copper becomes coated with a black layer on the outside and there is a slight increase in mass. When the foil is unfolded, the copper which was not in contact with the air is shiny, not blackened. This shows that the air was responsible for the blackening. The copper has reacted with part of the air. A more complicated experiment is to heat copper in a vacuum. Then it remains shiny and its mass does not change.

Both these reactions are discussed again in the next chapter.

Summary

1 Reversible changes are those where the product of the change can easily be turned back to its original form.

2 Changes of state such as melting, freezing, boiling, condensing and subliming are reversible changes.

3 Chemical reactions are changes in which new substances are formed. Some chemical reactions are reversible. Examples are the decomposition of hydrated copper sulphate and hydrated cobalt chloride.

4 The presence of water may be tested using anhydrous copper sulphate (white $\rightarrow$ blue) or cobalt chloride paper (blue $\rightarrow$ pink). Pure water may be recognized by its steady boiling point at or near 100 °C.

5 Permanent changes are those which are not easily reversed.

6

Change of mass on heating a substance	What has occurred?
none	no change at all or a physical change only (e.g. melting)
loss	gas given off
gain	substance has reacted with part of the air

7 Common gases which are given off when solids decompose are:
steam (test: condenses back to water),
oxygen (test: rekindles a glowing splint),
carbon dioxide (test: turns limewater milky).

Questions

1 From the following list of words fill in the blank spaces in the passage: blue, green, pink, white, yellow, acid, alcohol, vapour, water, boiled, concentrated, condensed, dissolved, melted.

When red ink is put into a flask and ...., a .... is given off at 100 °C. This condenses in the Liebig condenser to give a clear, colourless liquid. When the liquid is mixed with anhydrous cobalt chloride, the cobalt chloride changes colour from .... to .... What is left in the flask is .... red ink. When .... is added to this, normal red ink is again obtained.

2 When hydrated cobalt chloride is heated, it turns blue and water is given off.
   a Draw a diagram of apparatus suitable for heating the cobalt chloride and collecting the water.
   b What test would you do to show that pure water had been given off?
   c How would you discover whether the cobalt chloride gains mass, loses mass or remains the same?
   d What result would you expect in **c** and why?
   e What would you do to show that the decomposition is reversible? What would you expect to observe?

3 Which of the following changes are reversible and which are permanent?
   a The melting of salol.
   b The boiling of ethanol.
   c The sublimation of iodine.
   d A candle burning.
   e Salt dissolving in water.
   f The freezing of water.
   g Cobalt chloride paper turning pink.

Liquid	Boiling point (°C)	Action on cobalt chloride paper
A	101	stays blue
B	105	turns pink
C	100	turns pink
D	57	stays blue

4 The results in the table on the left were obtained with four colourless liquids A, B, C and D.
   a Which of the four is pure water?
   b Which of the four is impure water?
   c Which would turn anhydrous copper sulphate blue?

5 a Explain to a younger brother, who has not been taught any science, the difference between melting and dissolving.
   b Your mother claims that when sugar is added to a cup of *hot* tea, it melts. How would you try to discover whether she is right?

6 Write sentences which include each of the following words. You may include more than one of the words in the same sentence. The sentence should convey some idea of the meaning of the word.
Sublime, hydrated, decompose, distil, solvent, anhydrous, reversible.

7 Blue crystals of copper sulphate appear to be quite dry, but when they are heated water vapour is given off and they lose mass. The residue left after heating is a white powder. When water is added drop by drop to this white powder, the water is absorbed and the powder gets quite hot.

In order to find what proportion of the crystals consisted of water, a weighed sample was heated in a crucible. The results were:

mass of crucible	= 14.20 g
mass of crucible + copper sulphate crystals	= 19.20 g
mass of crucible + white powder after heating	= 17.40 g

a Find the mass of water in 100 g of the crystals as follows:
  (i) Work out the mass of copper sulphate crystals.
  (ii) Work out the mass of water in the crystals.
  (iii) Work out the mass of water in 100 g of crystals.
b If you were doing this experiment, how would you know that the copper sulphate had been heated for long enough to drive out all the water?
c Why did the white powder get hot when water was added to it?
d A student doing the experiment was impressed by the rise in temperature and suggested that this might be a useful method of producing heat energy. What do you think of this suggestion?

8 4.99 g of the purple solid chrome alum are heated. Water is given off and the solid turns green. Heating is continued until no more water comes off. The green solid is found to weigh 2.83 g.
a Sketch an apparatus that you could use to collect the water which is given off.
b How would you prove that the liquid you collected was water?
c What mass of water would you expect to be given off?
d When water is added to the green solid, it stays green. Do you think that the solid is anhydrous chrome alum or do you think that there has been a permanent chemical change?

9 Three different solids A, B and C behave as follows when heated:
A melts, but does not decompose or vaporize;
B gives off oxygen gas;
C gives off some water vapour, but suffers no further change.
a State in each case what changes in mass you would expect (gain, loss or no change) when the solids A, B and C are heated.
b Explain how it is possible for a substance to gain mass when heated in air.
c Name one substance which does gain in mass when heated in air.

10 When sodium hydrogencarbonate is heated, steam and carbon dioxide are given off.
  a Draw a labelled diagram of an apparatus you could use to heat the crystals and to try to collect both water and carbon dioxide.
  b Give a test (and its result) for:
    (i) water,
    (ii) carbon dioxide.

11 The manufacturers of a certain washing powder claim that when it is placed in boiling water oxygen is given off.
  a Give a labelled sketch of the apparatus you could use to test this claim and collect the gas given off.
  b How would you test that the gas was oxygen?

12 The apparatus shown in the diagram (Fig 3.9) was used for heating various solids.

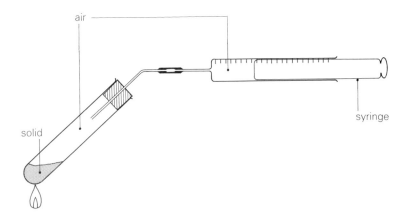

Fig 3.9.

  a Before heating, the syringe was half full of air. After heating for about five minutes, the apparatus was cooled back to room temperature, and the change in the volume of gas in the syringe was observed. The whole experiment was done four times using the four solids listed below, and starting with fresh apparatus each time. For each case, state what happened to the volume of gas in the syringe as a result of heating the solid:
    (i) copper foil,
    (ii) dry sand,
    (iii) potassium permanganate,
    (iv) copper sulphate crystals.
  b In cases (i) and (iv) above, what would you *see* happening to the solid while it was being heated?
  c In cases (i) and (iii) above, what would happen to the mass of the solid? Explain your answers briefly.

13 The table overleaf is the laboratory record of a student who had been finding out what happened when certain solids were heated in air.

Name of solid	Colour before heating	Colour during heating	Colour after heating	Mass change of solid	Effect of adding water to cold residue
cobalt chloride	red	blue	blue	loss	dissolves to give red solution
zinc oxide	white	yellow	white	none	does not dissolve
nickel carbonate	green	black	black	loss	does not dissolve
potassium chloride	white	white	white	none	dissolves to give colourless solution
iron wire	grey	red hot	black	gain	does not dissolve

On the evidence provided in the table:

a Which of the substances were affected by the heating?

b Which substance was temporarily affected during the time it was being heated?

c Is potassium chloride soluble in water? Justify your answer.

d Where could the increase in mass of the iron wire have come from?

e On the evidence above, is it possible to say whether or not nickel carbonate is soluble in water?

f What substance could have been the cause of the loss in mass when cobalt chloride was heated?

14 The three statements below about heating substances are correct, but the reasons given are not. In each case:

a Describe simple experiments you could do to show that the reason given is wrong.

b Write out the correct reason.

Statement	Incorrect reason
(i) potassium permanganate loses mass when heated	part of it is destroyed
(ii) copper turns black when heated in air	the Bunsen flame deposits soot on it
(iii) copper sulphate crystals give off water on heating	they must have been damp to start with

Additional material – when solids decompose

Experiment 3.4
Heating copper sulphate (See Section 3.5)

1 Label two clean test-tubes A and B.

2 Weigh the two test-tubes (masses *A1* and *B1*).

3 Add about 3 g of copper sulphate to one and more to the other.

4 Weigh both test-tubes again (masses *A2* and *B2*).

5 In turn, gently heat both test-tubes with a Bunsen burner until no more water is given off and the insides of the test-tubes are dry.

6 Allow the test-tubes to cool and weigh again (masses *A3* and *B3*).

7 For each test-tube, calculate:
a the mass of copper sulphate before heating
(*A2 −A1, B2 − B1*).
b the mass of copper sulphate after heating
(*A3 − A1, B3 − B1*).

8 Divide the mass from **7b** by the mass from **7a** for each test-tube.

What do you notice about your results? They should be the same for each test-tube.

Plotting graphs

If all the members of your class heat copper sulphate, weighing the tube before and after the experiment, you can present their results on a graph, plotting *mass of anhydrous copper sulphate* against *mass of hydrated copper sulphate*. If the results are in proportion (as they should be), they will lie on a straight line that passes through the origin, as shown in Fig 3.10 overleaf.

When plotting any graph it is a good idea to do it in a series of steps.

1 Choose the scales in order to make the best use of the paper. Look for the greatest value of each of the two things you are plotting. This will tell you the largest number you need on each axis. Then pick a scale from which you can easily read values: for example, let one big square on the graph paper be 1 g, 2 g or 5 g, (or 0.1 g, 0.2 g, 0.5 g) but not 3 g or 6 g (or 0.3 g, 0.6 g) and certainly not 3½ g.*

2 Label each axis clearly and include the units.

3 Plot the points carefully, using small crosses.

4 Decide whether the line should go through the origin. In this case if no copper sulphate is heated, no solid will be left, so the line should go through the origin.

5 Decide whether any of the points don't fit. In this example point K was obtained by a student who was late for the lesson and did not finish.

6 Decide whether a straight line or a curve best fits the points. Do not join all the points.

* The figures for the variables *you* decide (not the ones that are produced by the experiment) are usually plotted on the horizontal axis (*x*-axis).

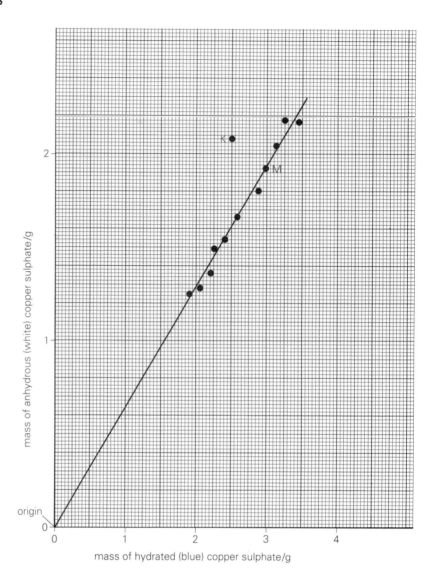

Fig 3.10.

mass of anhydrous (white) copper sulphate/g (y-axis)

mass of hydrated (blue) copper sulphate/g (x-axis)

7 Draw the line. This is called the **line of best fit** and, if it is
straight, it is called the **best straight line** through the points.
A transparent ruler is very useful to help you draw the line.
Because of experimental error, not all the points lie on the line.
It is impossible to weigh with complete accuracy and this
causes a scatter of points around the line. They should average
out with about the same number of points on either side of
the line.

All decomposition reactions obey the same rules. If *mass of
residue* is plotted against *mass heated* we shall always get a
straight line through the origin.

Gas densities

Density measures the mass of a 'unit volume'. In our usual units
this means it is the mass in grams of one cubic centimetre (cm^3)

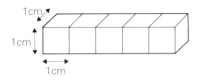

Fig 3.11 Five cubes, each of volume 1 cm³.

Fig 3.12 Heating potassium permanganate.

of substance. For example, each of the small cubes in Fig 3.11 has a volume of 1 cm³. If the whole lump weighs 20 g, then the

$$\text{mass of 1 cm}^3 = \frac{20}{5} = 4 \text{ g}.$$

We say that the density is 'four grams per cubic centimetre' which we write as 4 g/cm³. So:

$$\text{density} = \frac{\text{mass}}{\text{volume}}$$

Six 1 cm³ cubes of the same substance will weigh 24 g and the density is

$$\frac{\text{mass}}{\text{volume}} = \frac{24}{6} = 4 \text{ g/cm}^3$$

the same as before, because it is the same substance. An *irregular lump* of substance with volume 8 cm³ will weigh 32 g and so its density will still be 4 g/cm³.

To measure the density of a gas we need to know the *mass* of a certain *volume*. We can measure the volume in a gas syringe or graduated tube, but weighing gases is difficult. However, if the gas is given off when a solid decomposes, we know that the *mass of the gas* is equal to the *mass lost by the solid*. Thus if the solid lost 0.1 g and the volume of the gas was 100 cm³, the density of the gas would be:

$$\frac{\text{mass}}{\text{volume}} = \frac{0.1}{100} = 0.001 \text{ g/cm}^3$$

Consider an example from an experiment where potassium permanganate is heated, giving off oxygen (using the apparatus shown in Fig 3.12).

mass of potassium permanganate before heating = 2.63 g
mass of residue after heating = 2.52 g
mass loss = 0.11 g
volume of gas in syringe at start = 2 cm³
volume of gas in syringe after heating = 84 cm³
volume of oxygen = 82 cm³
(room temperature 20 °C)

This means that 82 cm³ of oxygen weigh 0.11 g. The mass of 1 cm³ is given by:

$$\frac{\text{mass}}{\text{volume}} = \frac{0.11}{82} = 0.0013 \text{ g/cm}^3$$

Since this number is so small, it is usually expressed in grams per dm³ (litre); one dm³ is a thousand times as big as one cubic centimetre, so 1 dm^3 of oxygen will have a thousand times as much mass.

$$0.0013 \times 1000 = 1.3 \text{ g/dm}^3 \text{ at } 20\,°C$$

Gases expand when they are heated, so the temperature at which the measurement was made should also be given.

The second example is from an experiment where zinc carbonate gives off carbon dioxide when it is heated.

mass of zinc carbonate before heating	= 4.97 g
mass of residue after heating	= 4.80 g
mass of carbon dioxide	= 0.17 g
volume in syringe at the start	= 3 cm^3
volume in syringe after heating	= 96 cm^3
volume of carbon dioxide	= 93 cm^3
(room temperature 25 °C)	

thus the density of carbon dioxide $= \dfrac{0.17}{93} = 0.0018 \text{g/cm}^3$

$$= 1.8 \text{ g/dm}^3 \text{ at } 25\,°C$$

Since the amount of gas given off is *proportional* to the loss of mass, several experiments can be carried out and a graph plotted. Fig 3.13 shows a graph obtained by plotting *volume of oxygen* against *loss of mass*, for a number of experiments where potassium permanganate was heated. To work out the density

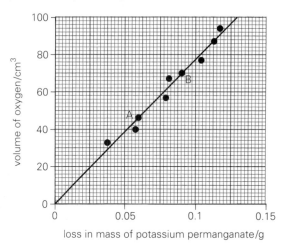

Fig 3.13.

we could take any point on the graph and divide the mass of the gas by the volume it occupies. For example point A,

density $= \dfrac{0.06}{46}$ g/cm^3; point B, density $= \dfrac{0.09}{70}$ g/cm^3. To

make the division sum easy, a convenient volume, for example 100 cm^3, can be used. The corresponding loss of mass can be read from the graph (0.13 g) even though no experiment gave as much as 100 cm^3 of gas. The calculation is now:

$$\text{density of oxygen} = \frac{\text{mass}}{\text{volume}} = \frac{0.13}{100} = 0.0013 \text{ g/cm}^3 \text{ at } 20\,°C$$

Measuring and errors

Even when a lot of care is taken, it is still impossible to avoid small errors when making measurements. When weighing it is often difficult to be more accurate than 0.01 g (this depends on the type of balance used). This does not matter much in a mass of 5.00 g, but it matters more if you are 0.01 g wrong when the value is 0.13 g as in the last example.

Gas volumes are measured in gas syringes. Here it is difficult to be more accurate than about 1 or 2 cm^3. Again, this is not too important in a value of 90 cm^3, but it makes a big difference if the value is only 10 cm^3. A measuring cylinder (used to measure volumes of liquid) can be read to similar accuracy.

Errors of this sort tend to be *random*, that is, the values are sometimes too high and sometimes too low. If we do an experiment enough times (as happens when a class pools its results) then the high and low values tend to cancel each other out and we get a more reliable answer.

It is valuable to plot a graph, because this shows which values are really wrong (for example point K in Fig 3.10) and which values cannot be avoided because the apparatus is not perfect. Also, a point on the line is more accurate than any individual result, because the line represents the average of the results.

Questions

1 Look at the graph in Fig 3.10 and at number **5** in the steps for plotting graphs on page 37 and explain why the point K occurs above the line, and not on it.

2 Six pairs of students heated some blue copper sulphate crystals in identical test-tubes. The crystals turned white and were found to lose mass. The students obtained the results below.

Mass of tube and blue crystals before heating (g)	Mass of tube and white powder after heating (g)
17.51	16.60
16.02	15.65
16.40	15.85
16.85	16.61
15.64	15.40
17.10	16.34

a Plot a graph of *mass of tube and contents before heating* against *loss in mass*, showing loss in mass on the vertical axis.
b Which group would you advise to repeat the experiment?
c What do you think was the probable cause of their error?
d Use the graph to work out the mass of the test-tube.
e Use the graph to work out the mass of white copper sulphate that could be obtained by heating 1 gram of the blue crystals.

3 All the members of the class heated samples of potassium permanganate and measured the volume of oxygen which evolved. Their results were:

Mass of tube and contents before heating (g)	Mass of tube and contents after heating (g)	Volume of oxygen (cm^3)
16.31	15.21	870
20.62	19.42	700
15.43	14.55	630
12.52	12.18	260
18.46	17.93	370
13.97	13.23	560
18.76	17.51	960

a Plot a graph of *loss in mass* of the potassium permanganate (on the horizontal axis) against *volume of oxygen.*

b Which of the points is obviously wrong? Three members of the class suggested reasons for this inaccurate result:
   (i) Too much potassium permanganate was taken and thus it did not all decompose.
   (ii) There was a leak in the syringe.
   (iii) The syringe was not at zero to start with.
   Consider each of these in turn and state why it could or could not have caused the inaccuracy.

c What mass would be lost in an experiment in which 100 cm^3 of gas was obtained?

d Work out a value for the density of oxygen at the temperature of the experiment:
   (i) In gram per cm^3.
   (ii) In gram per dm^3.

Time (min)	Mass of the test-tube (g)	Volume of oxygen (cm^3)
0	8.56	0
1	8.53	25
2	8.48	60
3	8.44	90
4	8.44	90
5	8.44	90

4 A student heats some potassium permanganate in a test-tube and collects the gas given off in a syringe. During the course of the experiment the test-tube is weighed and the volume of oxygen given off noted (see left).

a Plot a graph to show how the mass changes with time.

b How long does it take for all the potassium permanganate to decompose?

c How can the student be sure that all the potassium permanganate has decomposed at the end of the experiment?

d From the figures, calculate the density of oxygen in g/cm^3.

Chapter 4

The air

4.1 Introduction

At the end of the last chapter we saw that the disappearance of sulphur and the gain in mass of magnesium and copper when heated had something to do with the air. We must thus know something about air before we can explain what happened.

The air is a mixture of gases which can be separated by fractional distillation (Section 2.5). The most abundant (commonest) gas in the air is the unreactive gas nitrogen which accounts for 78 % (just under $\frac{4}{5}$) of the air. The next most common is oxygen (Section 3.8) which accounts for 20 % (about $\frac{1}{5}$) of the air. Then there is argon (about 1 %) together with even less of helium, neon, krypton and xenon. These five gases are very unreactive and are known as the noble (or inert) gases. Fig 4.1 shows the composition of air in a **pie chart**. The air contains water vapour and carbon dioxide (Section 3.9), but the quantities of these vary and they are never more than a very small percentage of the air.

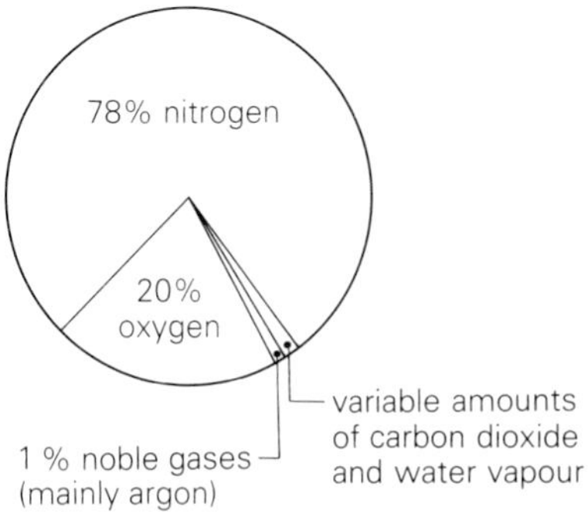

Fig 4.1 The gases of the air.

4.2 Oxygen and burning

Oxygen is the most reactive gas in the air. When a substance is heated in air and gains mass, it is therefore more likely to have reacted with the oxygen than with anything else. Evidence for this comes from several experiments:

1 We saw in the last chapter that, when a folded piece of copper is heated, the parts in contact with the air blacken. However, when a piece of copper is heated in nitrogen (or in air from which the oxygen has been removed) it remains unaffected.
2 Substances burn more vigorously in pure oxygen than they do in air.
3 An important experiment uses the apparatus shown in Fig 4.2 overleaf. Using syringes, air is passed over heated copper which is contained in a thin silica tube. The copper turns black and, as it does so, the volume of air decreases. However, when about $\frac{1}{5}$ of the air has been used up, there is no further change in volume. If some of the unreacted copper is heated, it does not turn black. These observations suggest that it is the

Fig 4.2 Measuring the volume change when air is passed over heated copper.

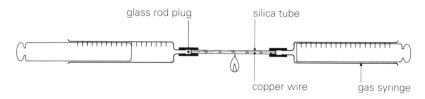

oxygen in the air which is used. This can be confirmed by disconnecting the apparatus and expelling the gas from one of the syringes. At the same time a glowing splint is placed near the nozzle of the syringe. The splint will go out; if the syringe had contained any oxygen the splint would have continued to glow.

So it is the oxygen in the air which is the active part. Nitrogen will react with other substances only at extremely high temperatures and the noble gases do not combine at all.

4.3 The formation of oxides

All these reactions produce a new substance. The original substance **combines** with the oxygen to form an **oxide**:

magnesium   +   oxygen   →   magnesium oxide
(see Section 3.11)

copper   +   oxygen   →   copper oxide (see Section 3.11)

phosphorus   +   oxygen   →   phosphorus oxide

Such a reaction with oxygen is known as **oxidation.**

These oxidation reactions are also known as **burning** or **combustion** and the oxides produced are called the **combustion products.**

4.4 Oxides of sulphur and carbon

Safety note

Sulphur dioxide is toxic. Use a fume cupboard.

While the oxides of magnesium, copper and phosphorus are all solids at room temperature, those of sulphur and carbon are gases. This explains why sulphur apparently disappears when it is heated in air, as we saw in Section 3.10. What happens is that the sulphur melts and then burns in air to form the new substance, sulphur dioxide (the *di-* here means 'two' – as also in carbon *di*oxide). The sulphur dioxide (which is responsible for the sharp smell) then mixes with the other gases in the air. The sulphur dioxide weighs more than the sulphur and this can be demonstrated if an apparatus similar to that of Fig 4.6 is used. A known mass of sulphur is burned and the gas is absorbed in sodalime. (The sodalime 'sucks up' the gas rather like a sponge sucking up water.) The increase in mass of the sodalime tubes gives the mass of the sulphur dioxide.

Carbon behaves in the same way. When it is burned it forms carbon dioxide, which can be detected by using limewater. Once again the carbon apparently disappears, though if wood charcoal is used a little ash remains because wood charcoal is not a pure form of carbon.

Air pollution

When coal and oil are burned in power stations, or in homes they release energy, carbon dioxide and, in the case of oil, water vapour. Unfortunately coal and oil are impure and contain sulphur which also burns to form sulphur dioxide. This is an obnoxious gas but, worse still, it is converted to sulphuric acid in the atmosphere (see page 79). Much research is being done, and much money is being spent, to try to cut down the amount of sulphur dioxide that gets away into the atmosphere.

At least as bad is the nitrogen dioxide from car engines. In a car engine the temperature becomes so hot that the two main gases in the air, nitrogen and oxygen, react together to form nitrogen oxide, which eventually turns into nitric acid.

Other problems are caused when the coal or oil do not burn completely. This produces carbon monoxide, a poisonous gas, and soot which consists of tiny particles of carbon. The soot sticks to everything and is responsible for the black buildings in areas where there is a lot of industry (needing a lot of energy and hence using a lot of fuel). After a particularly bad smog in 1953, Parliament passed new laws and the air is now much cleaner than it used to be. Smog was a lethal combination of smoke and fog. The fog droplets contained dissolved sulphur dioxide, nitrogen dioxide and other acids. Breathing was almost impossible, lungs were badly damaged and no one could see further than about a metre.

Even though conditions are now better, they are still far from perfect. The answer may be for mankind to obtain energy in ways other than by burning fuels.

Question
What sources of energy do we have that do not involve burning fuels? (If you are stuck, look up chapter 11 in *Physics 11–14*.)

Safety note

Nitrogen dioxide is toxic.

Safety note

Carbon monoxide is toxic.

4.5 The burning of compounds

If natural gas (methane) is burned in a flask (Fig 4.3 overleaf) *two* products of burning can be identified. One product is the condensation on the inside of the flask; this turns blue cobalt chloride pink and is therefore water. Water is the oxide of hydrogen (hydrogen means 'water former'). The flask can also be shown to contain carbon dioxide by shaking some limewater in it. We can therefore write:

Safety note

Methane is flammable

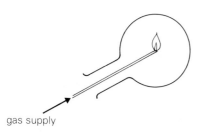

Fig 4.3 Burning natural gas in a flask.

Fig 4.4 Burning a candle under a beaker.

(a)

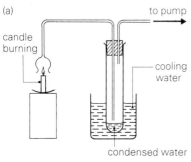

(b)

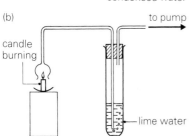

Fig 4.5 Detecting water and carbon dioxide in the products of combustion of a candle.

methane + oxygen → carbon dioxide + hydrogen oxide
water

It is thus reasonable to say that methane contains some carbon and some hydrogen. If it were a *mixture* of the two we should see little specks of carbon. We cannot because the carbon and hydrogen are chemically combined and are called a **compound**.

Carbon and hydrogen are called **elements** as they cannot be broken down into simpler substances. We can recognize elements when we burn them because they give one *oxide only*. Compounds, which consist of two or more elements combined together, usually give the oxides of those elements when they burn. You will find out more about elements in Chapter 8.

Candle wax is another example of a compound. By burning a candle it is possible to find out the elements it contains.

Experiment 4.1
Burning a candle

1 Light the small candle provided. Draw a labelled diagram of the top of the candle and the flame, showing as much detail as possible.

2 Place a beaker over the candle (Fig 4.4). Why does the flame go out? You may see a black stain on the top of the beaker. Where does this come from?

3 Use cobalt chloride paper to test the mistiness on the inside of the beaker for water. Write down the result. What does this tell you about the candle wax compound?

4 Think about how to test the gas in the beaker for carbon dioxide. Carry out the test and write down the result. What does this tell you about the candle wax compound?

5 Blow out the candle. Why does blowing cause the candle to go out?

The diagram shows the apparatus needed for *collecting* the products of a burning candle. In Fig 4.5a water condenses in the tube and can be tested by using cobalt chloride paper. In Fig 4.5b the limewater turns milky showing the presence of carbon dioxide.

The apparatus shown in Fig 4.5 can also be used to show that ethanol gives carbon dioxide and water when it burns. Thus it must contain carbon and hydrogen. In fact it also contains oxygen, but it is not possible to tell this by looking at the products of burning which get some of their oxygen from the air.

Not all elements react directly with the air to form their oxides and neither do all compounds burn in air. Many compounds containing carbon burn, but there are important exceptions such as tetrachloromethane (carbon tetrachloride) and trichloroethane (a dry-cleaning solvent).

Some carbon compounds which do burn in air are useful as **fuels**, since they are available in large quantities and transfer a lot of energy to the surroundings when they burn. They are concentrated sources of chemical energy. An important group of compounds are the **hydrocarbons**, which are compounds of just hydrogen and carbon as the name suggests. Examples are methane (natural gas), propane, butane (Calor gas), octane (one substance in car petrol) and benzene. These all give carbon dioxide and water when they burn.

When a compound burns, the products of combustion tell us something of the elements contained in the compound. For example, hydrocarbons burn to give carbon dioxide and water, and carbon disulphide burns to give carbon dioxide and sulphur dioxide. However, ethanol (which also contains oxygen) burns to give carbon dioxide and water, so it is not possible to identify all the elements (especially oxygen) from the combustion products.

4.6 Changes in mass on burning

When substances burn, they take in oxygen from the air and gain in mass. This is not at all obvious when ethanol is burned in a crucible for the ethanol disappears completely. However, if the apparatus shown in Fig 4.6 is used, the water and the carbon dioxide produced can be shown to have a greater mass than the ethanol burned. We have assumed that the carbon dioxide and water trapped by the sodalime all came from the burned ethanol, but some of it might have come from the air and would have been sucked in whether we were burning ethanol or not.

To test this we carry out what is called a **control experiment**: air is drawn through the apparatus for the same length of time as the ethanol took to burn. The U-tubes *do* gain in mass slightly, showing that some carbon dioxide and water vapour did come from the air. The gain in mass of the U-tubes in this experiment must be subtracted from the gain which was noticed when the ethanol was burned. However, it is still found that the carbon dioxide and water vapour produced by the burning ethanol weigh more than the ethanol did to start with.

Safety note

Ethanol is highly flammable.

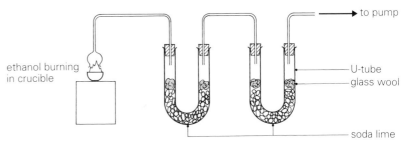

Fig 4.6 Collecting and weighing the products of combustion of ethanol.

This experiment can also be used to investigate the burning of a candle or sulphur (Section 4.4). Once again it is found that the oxides weigh more than the substance which was burned.

Safety note

Use a clean sterilized tube to blow down.

4.7 Breathing

When we breathe, we breathe out more carbon dioxide than we breathe in. You can show this using an apparatus like that in Fig 4.7. The limewater in the left-hand flask, through which the air

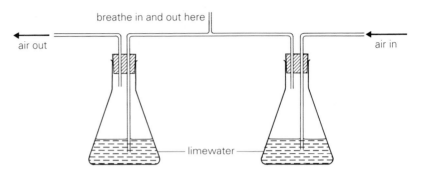

Fig 4.7 Breathing.

goes when we breathe out, goes milky before the limewater in the right hand flask. Do not think that in each breath we completely convert all the oxygen we breathe into carbon dioxide – we are not that efficient. The air we breathe out contains approximately 4% carbon dioxide and still 16% of oxygen.

Where does the carbon come from to make the carbon dioxide? It comes from carbon compounds (mainly carbohydrates and fat) which we oxidize to carbon dioxide and water in a process similar to burning:

carbohydrate + oxygen $\longrightarrow$ carbon dioxide + water

This is called respiration. It releases energy which we need to keep us warm, operate our muscles and to make other compounds (*Biology 11—14* Chapter 16). We obtain our carbohydrate and fat by eating plants and animals.

4.8 The carbon cycle

Carbon dioxide is made when:
a animals respire,
b plants respire,
c fuels are burned.
All these use up oxygen. Why doesn't the oxygen run out? Fortunately there is one process by which carbon dioxide is turned back into oxygen. This is called photosynthesis and it occurs when the sun shines on green plants. They are then able to carry out the reaction:

light energy + carbon dioxide + water $\longrightarrow$ carbohydrates + oxygen

Luckily there are so many green plants in the world that the oxygen level is maintained by this one process. If you were an astronaut looking at the globe from outer space you would see many green land areas where most of the surface was plants. One of the greenest would be the vast areas of the rain forests round the River Amazon in Brazil. These act as enormous 'oxygen factories' turning the carbon dioxide back into oxygen. Thus we ought to be worried that these forests are being cut down at an alarming rate to clear land for farming.

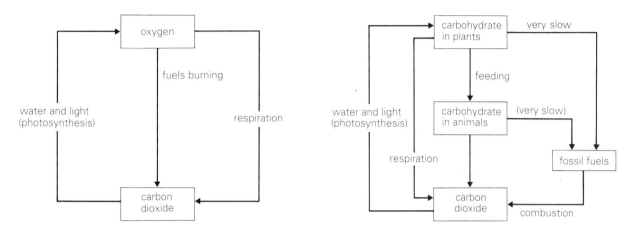

Fig 4.8 a The oxygen cycle
       b The carbon cycle.

Fig 4.8 shows how these activities lead to a cycle involving carbon dioxide and oxygen. The bodies of animals and plants have, over millions of years, turned into fossil fuels and these are shown too.

4.9 Nitrogen and its uses

Compared with oxygen, nitrogen is a very unreactive gas. We need nitrogen in our bodies to make proteins, but none of the vast amounts of nitrogen we breathe in (and out again) ever forms a compound in our bodies. We get our protein from eating plants and animals which also contain protein. Plants are able to absorb nitrogen compounds from the soil and some have bacteria in their roots which can turn nitrogen gas into its compounds. However, our intensive use of the soil often means that the bacteria cannot keep up and we must add nitrogen compounds as fertilizers.

Originally potassium nitrate from Chile was used, but now a major part of the chemical industry makes fertilizers for farmers. It does this by forcing the nitrogen in the air to react with other substances. For example, nitrogen and hydrogen can be made to react to form ammonia. This can be used as a fertilizer itself or used to form other nitrogen compounds which are fertilizers.

Summary

1 The air consists of nitrogen (78 %), oxygen (20 %), noble gases (1 %), carbon dioxide and water vapour (variable amounts).

2 Oxygen is the *active part* of the air. When substances burn in air they *combine* with oxygen to form their *oxides*. These are called *combustion products*.

3 *Elements* (which cannot be broken down to any simpler substance) burn to give single oxides.

4 *Compounds* consist of two or more elements **chemically combined** together. Those which burn usually give a mixture of the oxides of the elements which they contain.

5 When substances burn they gain in mass. If the oxides are gases they must be **absorbed** in a solid (for example sodalime) before they can be weighed.

6 *Fuels* are substances which release a lot of energy as heat when they are oxidized.

7 We breathe in oxygen, part of which oxidizes carbon compounds from our food. Thus we breathe out more carbon dioxide than we breathe in.

8 In daylight, plants remove carbon dioxide from the air and produce oxygen by a process called *photosynthesis*.

9 Nitrogen is a very unreactive gas, but plants need its compounds, in the form of *fertilizers*, to grow properly.

Background Reading

Lavoisier and the downfall of the phlogiston theory

Modern ideas of burning were put forward in 1774 by a French chemist called Antoine Lavoisier. Until that time chemists had believed that substances lost something called **phlogiston** when they burned. This **phlogiston theory** could be summarized:

$$\text{substance} \xrightarrow{\text{burning}} \underset{\text{(or ash)}}{\text{calx}} + \text{phlogiston}$$

This was presumably based on the observation that many substances (for example magnesium and wood) tend to crumble when they burn and look as though they have lost something.

As chemists began to weigh the substances they heated, the phlogiston theory became more difficult to uphold; how can substances *gain* mass on burning (as they do) while *losing* phlogiston? So sure were many chemists of the validity of the phlogiston theory that they invented ingenious ways around this

Fig 4.9 Lavoisier.

Safety note

Mercury is toxic.

problem, some even suggesting that phlogiston had negative mass!

About 1774 several chemists had in fact prepared the gas we now call oxygen by various methods; these men included Scheele, a Swedish chemist, and the Englishman Priestley. Priestley had decomposed mercury oxide by heating it and had obtained a gas in which candles and other materials burned more brightly than in air. He also noticed that a mouse lived longer in the gas and that his 'breast felt peculiarly light and easy for some time afterwards' when he tried breathing it. Priestley called the gas **dephlogisticated air** concluding that substances burned more vigorously because it took up their phlogiston readily. Priestley's main contribution was that he told Lavoisier of his discovery when they met in Paris in October 1774. Lavoisier repeated the experiment but realized it led not to an extension of the phlogiston theory, but to a new theory of burning—the one we hold today.

To verify this, he heated mercury in a furnace using a retort as shown in Fig 4.10. After a while he noticed the 'red calx of mercury' (mercury oxide) forming on the surface of the mercury. After 12 days no further change had occurred and the volume of air in the bell jar had fallen from 820 cm^3 to 690 cm^3. Thus the mercury had *taken in* part of the air when it formed its calx. He then took the mercury calx, scraping it away from the mercury, and heated it in a small retort. He collected 130 cm^3 of gas, exactly the volume lost by the air. He also showed that the gas had the same properties as Priestley's dephlogisticated air. When this gas was added back to the 690 cm^3 of gas in the bell jar, the resulting mixture could not be distinguished from ordinary air. All this led Lavoisier to put forward the theory that mercury *combined* with this newly discovered gas to form its calx.

mercury + oxygen ⇌ mercury oxide

He concluded that the gas Priestley had discovered was the 'active part' of the air. His name 'oxygen' means 'acid former' as he thought that all oxides were acidic (in fact only those of the nonmetals are, see Chapter 8).

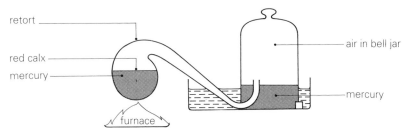

Fig 4.10 Lavoisier's experiment.

Antoine Lavoisier had been born into a wealthy French family in 1743, so he was about thirty when he conducted these experiments. His new theory of combustion was a turning point in the development of chemistry. He also contributed to the benefit of his country by helping to develop new farming methods.

However, he was not popular with the revolutionary powers because he was a tax collector. He was arrested on trumped up charges and sent to the guillotine on 8 May 1794. The judge said 'The Republic has no need of scientists'.

Priestley lived on until 1804 but he never gave up the phlogiston theory, though by then most other scientists had accepted Lavoisier's explanation of combustion.

Questions

1 What fraction of the air was used up in Lavoisier's experiment? Can you suggest why this is not the 20% you might expect?

2 Write a letter that Lavoisier might have written to try to convince Priestley that the phlogiston theory was wrong. (You need not write it in French!)

3 Imagine you were brave enough to stand up and defend Lavoisier in the French revolutionary court. What might you have said?

4 Write an article that might have appeared in a newspaper of the time describing the execution of Lavoisier and summarizing his contribution to science.

Questions

1 a The following substances are all gases. For each gas write 'yes' if you think that the gas is present in the air of the room in which you are sitting, and 'no' if you think it is not.
Nitrogen, hydrogen, carbon dioxide, water vapour.
  b What would be one effect you would notice if the amount of oxygen in the air were suddenly doubled?

2 a What happens to the mass of a piece of copper which is heated in air?
  b Why does this happen?
  c What happens to the mass of a piece of copper which is heated in nitrogen?

3 a What is the percentage of nitrogen in the air?
  b What compounds, essential to life, contain nitrogen?
  c How easily can the nitrogen in the air be converted into these compounds?
  d How do we get the nitrogen compounds we need?

4 Explain why:
  a When a piece of copper is folded and then heated in air, *only* the outside turns black.
  b When ethanol burns, nothing seems to be left at the end.
  c People are advised to roll themselves in a rug (or laboratory fire blanket) if their clothes catch fire.
  d During a fire, doors should be closed.

e When iron rusts in a limited volume of air, rusting stops when 20% of the air has been used up.

f When coal is burned, the ash weighs less than the coal; when magnesium burns, the ash weighs more than the magnesium.

5 Strontium metal burns in air to form a white powder which weighs more than the strontium.

a What is the chemical name of the powder?

b Why does it weigh more than the strontium?

6 A weighed coil of magnesium ribbon was heated in a crucible, which had its lid resting loosely on it. Although a little smoke was given off as the bottom of the crucible began to glow, it soon stopped coming off. Even when the lid was lifted slightly, no smoke appeared but the coil, now covered in white powder, appeared to glow more brightly. When they were cold the crucible and its contents were weighed again.

a What was the white powder covering the coil?

b What was the smoke?

c Why did the glow grow brighter when the lid was slightly lifted?

d If the crucible and its contents weighed more at the end of the experiment than they did before being heated, to what conclusion would you come?

e Why was the lid used?

7 Phosphorus is an element which burns fiercely in air to form a solid white oxide. When some phosphorus is burned in a flask which has been sealed with a bung, there is no change in the mass of the flask and contents until the bung is removed.

a Explain why the mass does not alter until the bung is removed.

b Would you expect the mass of the flask, bung and contents to increase or decrease as the flask was opened?

c What might you observe as the bung was removed?

8 Fire extinguishers work by:
cooling the fire,
or stopping the air reaching the flames,
(*or* a mixture of the two).

a Say why each of the methods works.

b Here are four substances which can be used to put out fires: carbon dioxide, foam, sand, water.

(i) By which method does each work?

(ii) Which substance would you use to put out a fire in delicate electrical machinery?

(iii) Which would you use to put out a fire in an oil spill on a concrete floor?

9 A tube containing copper was weighed. Using two syringes, 50 cm³ of air was passed backwards and forwards over the heated copper until the volume did not alter any more. Some of the copper was unchanged. After cooling, the gas volume was measured and the tube was weighed again.
  a Would the tube and copper have gained or lost mass?
  b What has happened to the copper?
  c What would you expect the volume of gas to be after cooling?
  d What was left in the syringes at the end?
  e What differences in your readings (mass and volume) would you expect if a greater mass of copper had been used?
  f Roughly what final volume would you expect if you had blown 50 cm³ from your lungs into the apparatus rather than taking 50 cm³ from the room?
  g What final volume would you expect if the syringes had contained a mixture of 10 cm³ oxygen and 10 cm³ nitrogen to start with?

10 When a candle burns, water vapour and a gas X are produced.
  a What is the gas X?
  b What test would you carry out to identify X? Describe what would happen.
  c Which two elements must be present in candle wax?
  d Name one other substance which will burn to give the same pair of products that a candle gives.
  e When a candle is burned under a glass chimney, all the products of combustion can be completely absorbed by some pieces of soda lime, supported on gauze, as shown in Fig 4.11. When the candle burns, will the total mass of the candle, chimney and contents increase, decrease or remain the same?
  f Explain your answer to **e**.
  g Some wax from a candle is heated carefully until it boils. It is found to start boiling at 320 °C, but does not completely boil away until the temperature has reached 400 °C. Suggest an explanation for this.

11 A student wishing to find out how much oxygen there is in air, connected two syringes by a piece of tubing filled with copper wire. At the start of the experiment there were 100 cm³ of air in the right-hand syringe and the copper was then heated strongly. Every time the air passed backwards and forwards over the heated copper, the student recorded the volume in the right-hand syringe. After six readings heating was stopped, and the air passed over three times more. The results at the top of page 55 were obtained:
  a Draw a graph to show how the volume of the gas remaining varied with the number of times the air was passed over the heated copper.
  b At what stage had the reaction ceased?

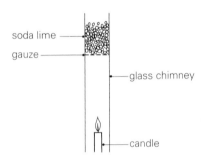

soda lime

gauze

glass chimney

candle

Fig 4.11.

Volume in right-hand syringe	Number of times the air had been passed backwards and forwards
100 cm^3	0
94 cm^3	1
90 cm^3	2
87 cm^3	3
85 cm^3	4
83 cm^3	5
83 cm^3	6 heating stopped here
82 cm^3	7
80 cm^3	8
80 cm^3	9

   c Can you suggest why the volume of the gas decreased slightly after heating was stopped?

   d What gas remains in the syringe?

   e What value do these figures give for the percentage of oxygen in the air?

12 The apparatus in Fig 4.12 can be used to show that carbon dioxide and water are produced when ethanol is burned.

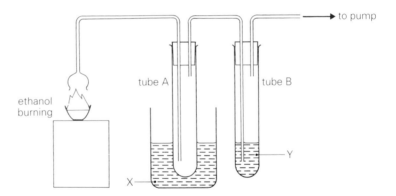

Fig 4.12.

   a Suggest what substance X might be.

   b Water collects in tube A and must have left the flame as a gas. What has happened to it to make it visible in tube A?

   c How would you show that the substance in tube A was water?

   d What would the substance Y be?

   e How would this substance show that carbon dioxide was present?

   f Why must tube A come before tube B?

   g What would you see in tubes A and B if the experiment were repeated, but with the burning ethanol removed so that only air was drawn through the apparatus?

13 Your grandfather says that 'gas fires dry the air'. Is this the case? (Natural gas is a compound of carbon and hydrogen.) Explain the situation to your grandfather.

14 a What experiments would you do to show that we breathe out more carbon dioxide than we breathe in? (Remember that air contains a little carbon dioxide.)

b Where does the extra carbon dioxide come from?

c Which gas is less common in the air that we breathe out than in the air we breathe in?

15 Give one good reason for not using the following as fuels:

a petroleum,

b coal,

c wood.

16 a Give two ways in which carbon dioxide in the atmosphere is increased and one way in which it is decreased.

b Is the amount of carbon dioxide in the atmosphere increasing or decreasing?

c What steps could be taken to reduce the amount of carbon dioxide in the atmosphere?

Chapter 5   **Chemical reactions**

5.1 Chemical changes

The reactions described in the last two chapters have all been chemical changes. If a chemical change takes place, the **products** of the reaction have very different chemical properties from the **reactants** (the substances which react together). Let us consider a few examples

1 Sulphur reacts with the oxygen in the air.

sulphur	+	oxygen	$\longrightarrow$	sulphur dioxide
yellow solid		colourless gas		colourless gas
		no smell		sharp smell
melts at 119 °C		boils at − 183 °C		boils at − 10 °C

An entirely new substance has been produced from the original sulphur and oxygen. They have not mixed but have *reacted* together to form the compound sulphur dioxide.

2 The loss of carbon dioxide from copper carbonate.

$$\text{copper carbonate} \xrightarrow{\text{heat}} \text{copper oxide} + \text{carbon dioxide}$$

copper carbonate	copper oxide	+	carbon dioxide
green solid	black solid		colourless gas

Here the copper carbonate changes chemically (in this case, **decomposes**) into the products which have very different properties from the reactants. (Copper carbonate is obviously not a mixture of copper oxide and carbon dioxide.)

3 The air consists mainly of the two colourless, odourless gases, oxygen and nitrogen. In the air these are *mixed* together and the properties of the air are a mixture of the properties of oxygen and the properties of nitrogen. If air is raised to a very high temperature (as, for example, in a lightning flash) a chemical reaction occurs and a **compound** is formed:

nitrogen	+	oxygen	$\longrightarrow$	nitrogen dioxide
colourless gas		colourless gas		brown gas
no smell		no smell		distinct smell

The product is very different from the mixture of nitrogen and oxygen in air. Air can be separated into nitrogen and oxygen by fractional distillation (see Section 2.5) but a chemical reaction is needed to break down the compound nitrogen dioxide.

Safety note

Sulphur dioxide is toxic.

Safety note

Copper carbonate is harmful.

Safety note

Nitrogen dioxide is toxic.

Safety note

Iron sulphide is harmful.

4 As a final example, consider a mixture of iron and sulphur, part metal and part yellow solid. The iron can be separated by using a magnet, or the sulphur can be dissolved in a suitable solvent. However, when the mixture is heated in a fume cupboard a reaction occurs and a *compound*, iron sulphide, is formed:

iron	+	sulphur	⟶	iron sulphide
black powder		yellow powder		black powder
conducts electricity		nonconductor		nonconductor
insoluble in		soluble in		insoluble in
all solvents		suitable		all solvents
		solvents		

The iron cannot be removed from the iron sulphide by a magnet and no part of it is soluble. Once again the product is very different from the reactants and cannot be separated except by a chemical reaction.

Summary

A *mixture* of substances has the properties of those substances and can usually be separated by physical methods (for example, sieving, filtering, dissolving, distilling, etc.).

A *compound* has its own properties and can only be broken down by a chemical reaction. A chemical reaction results in different substances with different properties being formed.

Background Reading

Chemical reactions all round us

We take chemical reactions so much for granted that we may not even realise that they are chemical reactions. When an apple ripens, the sour substances change into sweeter ones and there is often a colour change from green to red. The same sort of chemical changes go on in the leaves on the apple tree during autumn. If we cut open the apple, substances in the juice react with the oxygen in the air and turn brown; adding lemon juice or heating the apple cause other changes and so the browning reaction does not occur.

The kitchen provides many examples of chemical reactions, for cooking is a branch of chemistry: the fermentation reaction in baking and brewing, the hardening of egg white, the browning of pastry are familiar examples where the products of the reactions have very different properties from those of the reactants.

Other examples of chemical reactions at home include painting, glueing, plastering and polishing, all of which involve the formation of a new product. Some of these are quite complicated.

5.2 Evidence for chemical reaction

It is often easy to tell that a reaction has occurred by observing that the *properties* have changed. For example, from Section 5.1 evidence that a reaction had occurred would be:

1 Sulphur dioxide has a smell which is different from that of sulphur or oxygen.
2 Copper carbonate, which is green, gives a black solid when it has been heated.
3 Nitrogen and oxygen (colourless gases) react to form nitrogen dioxide (a brown gas).
4 Iron and sulphur (black and yellow specks) react to form iron sulphide (all black).

   Other examples we have met earlier are:

5 Dry blue copper sulphate crystals give a white powder and water when heated.
6 Magnesium (shiny metal) and oxygen (gas) react to form magnesium oxide (white powder).

Fig 5.1 Magnesium burning in air.

As many chemical reactions release energy when they occur, it is also possible to detect a reaction in this way. For example, when magnesium burns in air, energy is released, light is given out (Fig 5.1) and the surroundings are warmed.

The commonest way in which energy is released during chemical reactions results in warming the surroundings. Anhydrous copper sulphate reacting with water becomes warm and magnesium reacting with oxygen gets very hot. One reason why burning reactions are so useful to us is their ability to heat things up.

Light is also given out during reactions; magnesium reacting with oxygen gives white light, sulphur burning in oxygen gives a blue flame and candlelight was used as a source of illumination for many years. Another form of energy which is sometimes observed is sound; for example, the pop when hydrogen reacts with oxygen or the bang resulting from a chemical explosion.

It is therefore possible to use eyes, ears and nose to detect a reaction. However, the most valuable sense in these cases is that of touch. It becomes second nature for a chemist to touch a test-tube to try to detect the temperature rise which shows that a chemical reaction has almost certainly taken place.

5.3 The masses of substances which react

When copper is *mixed* with sulphur any amount of copper can be mixed with any amount of sulphur. 1 gram of copper could be mixed with 10 grams of sulphur, or 5 grams of copper could be mixed with 1 gram of sulphur, and so on. However, when copper *reacts* with sulphur it can only do so in one ratio. It is found that 1 gram of copper always reacts with just less than $\frac{1}{2}$ gram of sulphur; the masses of the elements will always be present in the same *proportion* in the copper sulphide which is formed. A compound always contains its elements combined in a definite proportion.

When magnesium reacts with oxygen, the masses of each substance which combine are in proportion. Magnesium can be burned in a crucible (Fig 5.2). The lid must be lifted from time to time to let in more oxygen, but the experimenter must take care to avoid losing magnesium oxide as a white smoke. The magnesium and the crucible (plus lid) are weighed separately before the experiment, and the crucible, lid and magnesium oxide are weighed at the end. The mass of magnesium oxide can be worked out by subtracting the mass of crucible and lid from the second weighing. Several of these experiments can be done and the results presented as a graph by plotting *mass of magnesium* against *mass of magnesium oxide* (Fig 5.3). The graph should be a straight line which passes through the origin. This shows that

Safety note

Anhydrous copper sulphate is harmful.

Safety note

Do not look directly at burning magnesium.

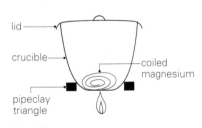

lid
crucible
coiled magnesium
pipeclay triangle

Fig 5.2

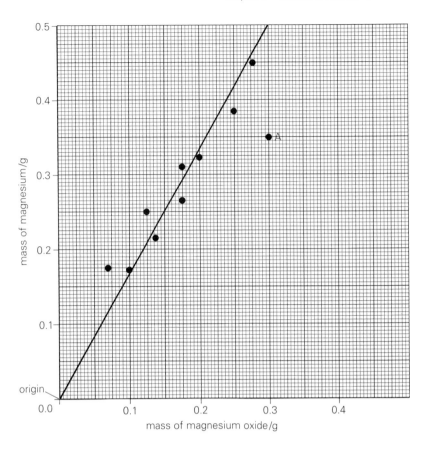

Fig 5.3

the masses of magnesium and the corresponding masses of magnesium oxide are always in the same proportion. If a graph is plotted of *mass of reactant* against corresponding *mass of product* in a chemical reaction, a straight line will always be obtained.

5.4 Speeding up chemical reactions

We know from cooking meals that reactions go faster if you increase the temperature. When we want the food to change, we heat it. If we want to slow down the reactions that spoil the food, we keep it in a refrigerator or freezer.

What else can we do to speed up a reaction? One method is to increase the amount of contact between the reacting chemicals. When heated, breadcrumbs go brown faster than a piece of toast does. The crumbs have a larger *surface area*. If you have a pill of medicine which you want to dissolve more quickly, you break it up into small pieces. Again this increases the surface area.

Safety note

Manganese dioxide (black manganese oxide) is harmful.

Fig 5.4 The preparation of oxygen.

We can also increase the *concentration* of one of the reacting chemicals. If we burn substances in pure oxygen rather than air, they react faster. Oxygen in the air is diluted by the other gases and thus reacts more slowly.

Another way of speeding up reactions is to add substances called **catalysts**. These speed up reactions but turn back into the same substance at the end of the reaction. An example is found in the preparation of oxygen from hydrogen peroxide (Fig 5.4). Hydrogen peroxide is a solution which decomposes very slowly to give oxygen – you can sometimes see the odd bubble. When it is mixed with black manganese oxide it gives off oxygen much faster. All the black manganese oxide can be recovered at the end of the experiment – it has acted as a catalyst.

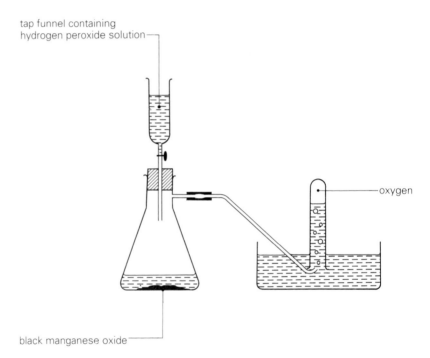

Catalysts are important in living things too. Here they are called enzymes. You can read about enzymes in *Biology 11–14* Chapter 4.

If sugar solution is placed in the apparatus shown in Fig 5.5 and some yeast is added, a process called fermentation begins to occur. The limewater in the tube gradually turns milky showing that carbon dioxide is produced (see Section 3.9). This is a result of sugar reacting with water to form ethanol and carbon dioxide, catalysed by enzymes from the yeast. A wide variety of alcoholic drinks is produced by this method. (See page 20.)

Fermentation is used by bakers. Yeast is mixed with flour and water. The yeast ferments the starch in the flour and the dough expands. This is caused by the carbon dioxide pushing the dough apart to make a more open structure.

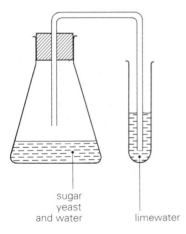

Fig 5.5 Fermentation.

Summary

1 The differences between mixtures and compounds may be summarized.

Mixtures	Compounds
may be separated by physical methods	separated by chemical reactions only
have properties of the substances which are mixed together	have their own properties
substances can be mixed in any proportion	substances react to form compounds in a definite proportion

2 Chemical reactions can be recognized from the following signs:
a New substance is formed.
b Temperature rises and to read and/or light is emitted.

3 To speed up a chemical reaction:
a Powder a solid.
b Make a solution more concentrated.
c Heat it.
d Add a catalyst.

4 Biological catalysts are called enzymes. The enzymes in yeast catalyse the fermentation of sugars to ethanol and carbon dioxide.

Background Reading

A typical day

Just consider an ordinary day. You get up and wash with water (made safe with chlorine, a chemical) and soap (made by reacting an oil with alkali). You clean your teeth with toothpaste (which will contain one or several chemicals). Your clothes may be made from nylon, Terylene, or acrylic material (fibres made from reacting two chemicals together). They will have been dyed with coloured compounds made in chemical reactions. And so to breakfast when you may eat toast (you can smell the different compounds made by heating) or bacon ('cured' in nitrite or nitrate solutions) or drink milk (treated by pasteurisation to prevent it going 'off', to prevent nasty reactions taking place) and then...

Question
Carry on with an account of a typical day, mentioning the influence of chemical reactions wherever you can.

Questions

1 When brown copper reacts with yellow sulphur, a glow spreads through the test-tube and a black solid is left.
  a Why is there a glow?
  b Is the black solid a compound (copper sulphide) or a mixture of copper and sulphur? Give reasons for your answer.
  c Why are the amounts of copper and sulphur important in this experiment?

2 When a match is struck, it burns.
  a How many senses could tell you that a chemical reaction is taking place?
  b What would each sense tell you?

3 Are the following examples of chemical reactions or physical changes? Give reasons for each of your answers.
  a A gas fire burning.
  b An electric fire getting hot.
  c Cobalt chloride turning from pink to blue when heated.
  d Ice turning to water when heated.
  e Salt dissolving in water.
  f Carbon (charcoal) burning in oyxgen.
  g A copper roof slowly turning green over the years.

4 A bright red powder (a metal oxide) is heated; a colourless gas is produced and a yellow residue remains.
  a What evidence do you have that a chemical reaction is taking place?
  b What do you think the colourless gas is?
  c How would you test for this gas? What would you expect the result to be?

5 a Give two reasons for believing that the addition of water to anhydrous copper sulphate results in a chemical reaction.
  b Give two reasons for believing that magnesium oxide is a compound and not a mixture of magnesium and oxygen.

6 Say, giving your reasons, whether you think the following are mixtures or compounds.
  a Milk.   **d** Copper oxide.
  b Ice.   **e** Carbon dioxide.
  c Orange juice.   **f** Paint.

7 5 grams of calcium combine with 2 grams of oxygen to form 7 grams of calcium oxide. Assuming that this is the only compound formed between calcium and oxygen, how much calcium oxide would you expect to get from:
  a 10 grams calcium and 4 grams oxygen?
  b 10 grams calcium and 2 grams oxygen?
  c 5 grams calcium and 4 grams oxygen?

8 Refer to the graph in Fig 5.3.
   a Explain in your own words why the graph is a straight line.
   b Why was the point A ignored when the line was drawn?
   c What mistake may have been made by the group who obtained point A?
   d Using your graph, work out the mass of oxygen which combines with 0.1 g magnesium.
   e How much oxygen would combine with 1 g of magnesium?
   f A class of students repeat the experiment but they use magnesium from an old sample which is already partly oxidized on the surface. They plot their results, *mass of magnesium taken* against *mass of magnesium oxide* and they obtain a straight-line graph. Say, giving your reasons, where this line will be in relation to the line in Fig 5.3.

9 a If some milk is left out on a hot day, chemical reactions cause it to decompose. What evidence is there that these are chemical reactions?
   b If some milk is heated strongly in a saucepan it 'burns'. What evidence is there that this is a chemical reaction?
   c Are the reactions in **a** and **b** the same? Give reasons for your answer.

10 A lump of limestone fizzes when dropped into dilute hydrochloric acid.
   a State two ways in which you would try to make the fizzing faster.
   b Say why you chose these two ways.

11 Explain why:
   a Iron filings make a 'sparkler' effect when put into a flame. An iron poker in the same flame will just glow.
   b Milk goes sour more quickly in the summer than in winter.
   c Some frozen foods can be kept for months in a freezer but must be eaten within a few days if kept in a refrigerator.
   d It is easier to light a fire with twigs than with branches.

12 The following passage is taken from an article on 'Safety in the home'.
   Fat for cooking is normally used at about 200 °C at which temperature it is quite safe. If fat is heated above 240 °C, however, a blue smoke is produced above the fat and this easily ignites. Burning fat accounts for about 40 % of fire accidents in the home. If fat catches fire it should be covered with a pan lid or a damp cloth (after the gas or electricity has been switched off). It is important that water should not be thrown on to burning fat.
   a When food is boiled in water, at about what temperature is it cooked?
   b Why is it usually quicker to cook food by frying rather than by boiling?

c Why is it important not to heat fat above 240 °C?

d What would happen to a drop of water put into fat at 200 °C?

e What therefore would be the result of throwing water on to burning fat?

f Explain why covering a pan of burning fat with a damp cloth or a lid will put out the fire.

13 (Difficult) This question concerns a substance called hydrogen peroxide. You should be able to answer the questions from your general knowledge of chemistry and the information given.

A solution of hydrogen peroxide decomposes slowly to water and oxygen. The process may be speeded up by adding a catalyst such as copper oxide. (A catalyst speeds up a reaction but remains unchanged at the end.) The concentration of a solution of hydrogen peroxide is described (in a quaint way) as 'volume strength'. This is the ratio of the volume of oxygen to the volume of hydrogen peroxide, for example, 1 cm^3 of a 10 volume solution gives 10 cm^3 of oxygen.

You are given a sample of hydrogen peroxide solution.

a How would you show that oxygen was given off when the solution decomposed?

b Design an apparatus to determine the 'volume strength' of the hydrogen peroxide, saying what measurements you would make.

c 15 cm^3 of hydrogen peroxide solution gave 50 cm^3 of oxygen when it decomposed completely. What was the 'volume strength'?

d Discuss whether 'volume strength' is a good method of measuring concentration, rather than 'grams of hydrogen peroxide per cubic centimetre of solution'.

Explorations 1

Always discuss your plans with your teacher before starting any practical work

A A house has been burgled and among other items stolen is an expensive fountain pen. A suspect has such a pen when interviewed by the police. A forensic scientist compares the black ink from the pen with ink from cartridges found in the burgled house. How can this be done most easily?

Try out your method on the inks provided.

B A large chemical company based in Cheshire is interested in 'solution mining' – pumping water into the ground to dissolve sodium chloride and pumping the solution up again. They wish to know whether more sodium chloride dissolves in hot water than cold water. Try to find out how much dissolves at different temperatures. (Remember to make your tests 'fair'.)

C On page 5 it says: 'The size of crystals can be adjusted by cooling the solution at different rates. Slow cooling produces one or two large crystals, while fast cooling gives many very small crystals.'

Carry out an exploration to find out whether this is so.

Think how you will measure crystal size and 'how fast' the solution cools.

D Discover which gas comes out when you open a can of cola.
Is the gas given off faster when:
a The temperature is changed?
b The pH is changed?
c Sugar is added?

Think of ways of measuring the speed at which the gas is given off. Don't forget to take readings over a range of temperatures, pH or amount of sugar.

How can you present your results?

Can you think of any other conditions you can vary?

E If you put a beaker over a burning candle, the candle will go out. What do you think will happen if you lift the beaker a little, a little more and so on?

Explore and find out. Think how you will present your results.

How can you explain your findings? Discuss your explanation with others. Do they agree with you?

Safety note

Methylated spirits are highly flammable.

F Two ways of keeping coffee hot involve burning either a candle or methylated spirits under a Pyrex jug. Carry out experiments to discover which is the cheaper way of producing the same result (measured by getting the same temperature rise in the same mass of water in a beaker).

You will need some more information from your teacher (or the shops) before you can work out the result. Is the cheapest method necessarily the best way of keeping the coffee hot?

What further explorations could you do to find out?

G How does the burning of a candle depend on the length of its wick? Explore how long the wick must be for the candle to stay alight and how the rate of burning is affected.

H Investigate the factors that can increase the rate of fermentation. Try varying the temperature, the amount of yeast and the sugar concentration. Work out how you are going to measure how much fermentation has occurred. Be sure to design your experiments so that the comparisons are fair.

See if you can work out the answers to the following:

a Does the rate double if the amount of yeast doubles?
b Does the rate double if the concentration of sugar doubles?
c By how much do you need to raise the temperature of the solution to double the rate of fermentation?

Chapter 6   **Acids and alkalis**

Safety note

Many dilute acids, 0.2M to 1M potassium and sodium hydroxide, and ammonia (5M to concentrated) are irritants.

Safety note

This symbol represents substances which are corrosive. Concentrated acids, concentrated ammonia, potassium and sodium hydroxide of 1M or greater concentrations and most other alkalis even in dilute solution. Eye protection must always be worn

Table 6.1 The pH values of some common substances.

6.1 The pH scale

As you go through a chemistry course, you will find that the meaning of the word **acid** changes gradually. To start with we say that an acid is a substance which is sour to the taste, though tasting is to be avoided since many acids are poisonous. The word acid often suggests a substance which burns or corrodes, but many acids are quite harmless. Indeed much of what we eat and drink is acid and it would taste very dull if it were not. The 'opposite' of an acid is an **alkali**. Alkalis are often much more harmful than acids. They should be treated with great care; they can be especially damaging to your eyes. A substance which is neither acid nor alkali is described as **neutral**. The best example of a neutral substance is pure water.

The acidity and alkalinity of substances can be measured using the pH scale (note – small p, capital H). Neutral substances have a pH of 7, acids have values less than 7 and alkalis have values greater than 7. A very low pH means a very strong acid whereas a value between 3 and 6 shows a weak acid. The lower the value, the stronger the acid. The opposite applies to alkalis where very high values indicate strongly alkaline solutions. Note that the word *alkaline* is an *adjective* (describing word) and the word *alkali* is a *noun*. Thus we say 'an alkaline solution' but we speak of 'an alkali' not 'an alkaline'.

Laboratory	pH value		Home
hydrochloric, nitric and sulphuric acids	0		car battery acid
	1	strong acid	
iron (III) chloride	2		lemon juice
ethanoic acid			beer, sour milk
	3		eating apple
	4	weak acid	
ammonium chloride, carbon dioxide	5		
	6		fresh milk
	7	neutral	salt, sugar
sodium hydrogencarbonate	8		soap, baking powder
sodium ethanoate	9		'milk of magnesia'
	10	weak alkali	
ammonia	11		
limewater (calcium hydroxide), sodium carbonate	12		washing soda
	13	strong alkali	oven cleaner
sodium hydroxide, potassium hydroxide	14		

pH values exist only when the substance is dissolved in water. Thus a completely insoluble substance will not have a pH value. Indicators are used to measure pH values and these are described in Section 6.2.

Table 6.1 on the previous page shows the pH values of some substances found in the laboratory or in the home.

Background Reading

Safety note

Calcium oxide is corrosive.

The names of acids and alkalis

The word 'alkali' comes from the Arabic and means 'the ashes', since the ashes from burning plant and animal materials are alkaline. 'Kalium', the name most other languages use for potassium, is derived from alkali. The name 'potassium' comes from *potash* (potassium carbonate) which gets its name from the way it used to be made. Wood ashes were dissolved in water and the solution evaporated in pots. The old name for potassium hydroxide was **caustic potash**; 'caustic' means 'burning', and brings home the dangerous nature of potassium hydroxide. Sodium carbonate is called **soda** or **washing soda** to distinguish it from sodium hydroxide which is **caustic soda**.

Lime is the name given to alkaline substances containing calcium. Calcium oxide is known as **quicklime** or **caustic lime**; calcium hydroxide is known as **slaked lime, milk of lime**, and, in solution, as **limewater**. Calcium carbonate, which is much less soluble in water than sodium or potassium carbonates, is known as **limestone**. These compounds are considered again in Chapter 9.

Acids generally have much more obvious names. Sulphuric acid contains sulphur, though concentrated sulphuric acid used to be known as **oil of vitriol** and the adjective 'vitriolic' is still used today.

6.2 Indicators

It has been known for thousands of years that certain dyes change colour when an acid or an alkali is added to them. These dyes are therefore able to **indicate** the presence of an acid or an alkali. The word **indicator** often implies an acid – alkali indicator, but a substance such as cobalt chloride is also an indicator since it indicates the presence of water.

One of the first indicators was a substance called **litmus**, which was extracted from a species of lichen. In solutions where the pH is 5 or less, litmus turns red; in solutions of pH 8 or more, litmus turns blue, and between 5 and 8 it is a mixture of the two colours. Other indicators change colour at different pH values, as

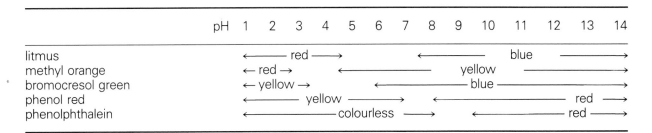

	pH	1	2	3	4	5	6	7	8	9	10	11	12	13	14
litmus		←——— red ———→					←		——	——	blue	————→			
methyl orange		← red →		←	——	——	——	——	yellow	——→					
bromocresol green		← yellow →			←	——	——	blue	—————	——→					
phenol red		←——— yellow ———→						←	——	——	red	——→			
phenolphthalein		←————— colourless ———→							←	——	——	red	——→		

Table 6.2 The colours of some indicators. In the 'gaps' shown the indicators are changing from one colour to the other.

shown in Table 6.2 which gives only a few of the hundreds of possible acid – alkali indicators.

By selecting six or seven indicators which change colour at different pH values, it is possible to make up a **universal indicator**. Such an indicator changes colour gradually over the whole pH range. Often the indicators are chosen so that the colours of the spectrum are obtained, starting with red at the acid end (red, orange, yellow, green, blue, indigo, violet). There are several universal indicators and they are not all quite the same; for example, the neutral colour is orange-yellow, yellow or green in three different universal indicators. The colours of indicators at various pH values are often shown on the bottles. The indicators are supplied in two forms. One is a solution in ethanol and the other is paper which has been soaked in the indicator solution and dried. This is often known as **pH paper**.

The simplest way to find an unknown pH is to use universal indicator. The substance with the unknown pH is dissolved in water, the indicator paper is added and half a minute is allowed for it to develop the true colour. If a solution of universal indicator is used, then one drop should be added to the unknown solution. If the pH of a gas is required, it may be tested with damp indicator paper.

Safety note

Dilute sodium hydroxide solution is corrosive.

6.3 Neutralization

Experiment 6.1
Neutralization

1 Put some dilute sodium hydroxide solution in a test-tube (a quarter full) and add two drops of universal indicator.

2 Carefully fill a pipette with dilute hydrochloric acid.

3 Hold the test-tube against a background of white paper and add a few drops of acid from the pipette.

4 You will see a swirl of red which disappears quickly as the solutions mix and react. Some of the alkali is **neutralized**.

5 Add more acid, a few drops at a time, and carefully shake the test-tube after each addition.

6 When the red colour doesn't disappear almost immediately, add the acid more carefully – one drop at a time.

7 Eventually, you will add a drop of acid and the whole of the liquid will remain a red colour. The pH goes from a high value to a low one.

8 If you feel the test-tube, you will notice that it is warm. Neutralization is an example of a chemical reaction that causes a rise in temperature.

Acids contain hydrogen, though their names do not always show this. An alternative name for hydrochloric acid is hydrogen chloride; sulphuric acid could be called hydrogen sulphate, and nitric acid, hydrogen nitrate. The names of alkalis usually end in 'hydroxide'. When an acid reacts with an alkali the hydrogen reacts with the hydroxide to give hydrogen hydroxide, which is usually called water. For example:

$$\underset{}{\text{sodium}\atop\text{hydroxide}} + \underset{}{\text{hydrogen}\atop\text{chloride}} \longrightarrow \underset{\text{water}}{\text{hydrogen}\atop\text{hydroxide}} + \underset{\text{common salt}}{\text{sodium}\atop\text{chloride}}$$

Both the substances produced are neutral.
Another example is:

$$\underset{}{\text{potassium}\atop\text{hydroxide}} + \underset{\text{sulphuric acid}}{\text{hydrogen}\atop\text{sulphate}} \longrightarrow \underset{\text{water}}{\text{hydrogen}\atop\text{hydroxide}} + \underset{}{\text{potassium}\atop\text{sulphate}}$$

The chlorides, sulphates and nitrates of metals are members of the large group of substances which chemists call **salts**. Sodium chloride, which is called salt in everyday language is only one of many salts in chemical language, so it is called **common salt** to distinguish it. You will find more about salts in Chapter 12.
The general equation for neutralization is:

$$\text{acid} + \text{alkali} \longrightarrow \text{salt} + \text{water}$$

Neutralization is certainly a chemical reaction since entirely new products are formed. Reactions in which the surroundings get hotter are said to be **exothermic**.
The equation is sometimes expressed:

$$\text{acid} + \text{base} \longrightarrow \text{salt} + \text{water}$$

A **base** is any substance which will react with an acid to form a salt. As we shall see in Section 8.4 metals form oxides which are bases. Most metals form oxides which, though they are insoluble in water, dissolve in acids just enough to neutralize them. Some metals form oxides which are soluble in water (and can still neutralize acids) and these are called **alkalis** (*soluble* bases). For example, sodium oxide is an alkali and it dissolves in water to form sodium hydroxide solution.

6.4 Applications of neutralization

People are often tempted to deal with the spillage of acids and alkalis using neutralization. If the spillage is on skin or clothing the neutralizing acid or alkali can be more dangerous than the substance which is spilled. The treatment here is washing and drenching with lots of water, since acids and alkalis are soluble in water.

If the spillage is on the bench or floor, then CLEAPSS recommends adding cat litter to the spill to absorb the liquid. This absorbant is then swept up into a bucket. Sodium carbonate (an irritant) and water are than put on the spillage area. These fizz (Chapter 12) if acid is still present. The reason for using a weak alkali is that it is easy to add too much. An excess of weak alkali is fairly harmless but an excess of strong alkali would be just as dangerous as the original spilled acid. For similar reasons a strong alkali is normally neutralized with citric acid.

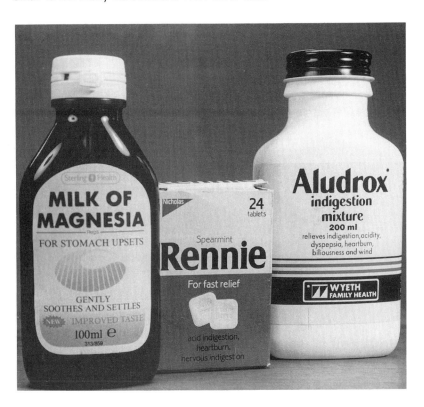

Fig 6.1 Antacids.

The stomach contains acid to help in the process of digestion. Sometimes too much acid is present and this is the commonest cause of indigestion ('acid stomach'). Some of the acid can be neutralized by a suitable very mild alkali. Milk of magnesia (a suspension of magnesium hydroxide in water) is one of the remedies which is used and such medicines are sometimes called **antacids**. If the indigestion persists, a doctor should be consulted.

Neutralization is important in agriculture. The pH of soil can be measured by first shaking it with water and barium sulphate. The very insoluble barium sulphate helps the soil particles to settle at the bottom of the tube and the solution which remains can then be tested with indicator in the usual way. Plants will grow only in soils where the pH value lies between 6 and 8. Many plants like a neutral pH, but some grow better if the pH is a little lower than 7, while others prefer a slightly alkaline pH.

Fig 6.2 Spreading lime on acid soil.

The more common problem is a soil which is too acid. In this case lime (calcium hydroxide) (Section 9.5) is added to neutralize the acid and increase the pH. Where soils are alkaline, acid fertilizers (ammonium nitrate or ammonium sulphate, which are added to replace nitrogen compounds lost by the soil) will lower the pH.

Summary

1 Acids are substances which have a sour taste and a pH less than 7.[*] Alkalis have a pH greater than 7.

* A further definition of an acid is a substance containing hydrogen which can be displaced by a reactive metal (see Section 10.8).

2 Substances which change colour in the presence of acids or alkalis are called *indicators*. A universal indicator shows different colours at different pH values.

3 The reaction between acids and alkalis is called **neutralization** and the general equation is:

acid + alkali ⟶ salt + water

4 Neutralization is important in curing acid stomach and acid soil.

Questions

1 a Explain how you would try to measure the pH of a colourless solution.
  b What values would you expect if the solution was:
    (i) Citric acid?
    (ii) Sodium chloride?
    (iii) Lime (calcium hydroxide)?

2 Four test-tubes contain dilute solutions of vinegar, washing soda, salt and sulphuric acid. You are not sure which contains which, so you add a few drops of universal indicator to each tube. From the following results, write down which substance is in each of the four tubes.

Tube	Colour	pH
1	red	2
2	orange	4
3	green	7
4	blue	10

3 There is an indicator which gives a yellow colour when added to lemon juice, a blue colour when added to milk of magnesia, and is green when added to pure water. Some of the indicator was added to a solution of slaked lime, and then hydrochloric acid was run in slowly, with shaking, until there was no further change of colour. Write down the three colours – yellow, blue and green – in the *order* in which they would be seen.

4 a What is meant by neutralization?
  b Why is neutralization important to a farmer?
  c How can neutralization be used to cure indigestion?

5 If a strong concentrated acid is spilt on the floor, a weak alkali, sodium hydrogencarbonate, is used to neutralize it.
  a How do we know when the acid has been completely neutralized by the sodium hydrogencarbonate?
  b Why is a strong alkali not used instead?
  c Why is water not used in *this* case?

6 a What is the first aid treatment if some strong concentrated acid is accidentally spilt on your hand?
  b Why is the acid not neutralized with an alkali?

7 An old wives mnemonic (memory aid) for treating bee and wasp stings is 'Bee – Bicarb: Vinegar – Vasp'. *Bicarb* is sodium hydrogencarbonate, a weak alkali; vinegar is a weak acid. What does the treatment suggest to you about the nature of bee and wasp stings?

8 An acid solution and an alkaline solution were mixed in the volumes given below and the resulting solutions were tested with an indicator. One mixture was neutral (pH 7), one had a pH value of 13 and the third had a pH value of 1.
  Copy out the table and fill in the column headed pH value.

Volume of acid (cm^3)	Volume of alkali (cm^3)	pH value
20	13	
20	15	
20	17	

9 a Suggest how you could measure the pH of a dry sample of soil in the laboratory.
  b What pH value would you expect acidic soil to have?
  c Which one of the following substances would be most suitable for neutralizing this acidic soil?
  Salt, water, lime, sand, vinegar.
  d What would happen to the pH of the soil when you added this substance?

10 There is a type of vegetable which is normally green in colour, but which turns red if cooked with vinegar.
  a Describe the method by which you would try to extract and separate the coloured substances in the green vegetable leaves.
  b How would you try to find out which of these coloured substances changes colour when treated with vinegar?
  c What is the name given to the type of substance which changes colour in this way?
  d Describe experiments which you could do to discover whether it is the cooking or the vinegar that turns the colour from green to red.

11 What products would you expect when the following react together?
  a Sodium hydroxide and nitric acid (hydrogen nitrate).
  b Potassium hydroxide and hydrochloric acid (hydrogen chloride).
  c Ammonium hydroxide and sulphuric acid (hydrogen sulphate).
  d In each case the salt is obtained as a solution in water. How would you obtain crystals of the salts?

12 a Use the information in Table 6.2 and the information below to deduce what you can about the pH values of:
   (i) Carbon dioxide solution.
   (ii) Ammonia solution.
   (iii) Sulphur dioxide solution.

Solution	Methyl orange colour	Litmus colour	Phenolphthalein colour
carbon dioxide	yellow	red	colourless
ammonia	yellow	blue	red
sulphur dioxide	red	red	colourless

b Do you think that a mixture of methyl orange, litmus and phenolphthalein would make a good universal indicator? Give your reasons.

13 This question is about some tests which a group of students did on some 'antiacid' tablets, sold for curing indigestion.
   They looked at the labels on the packets and wrote down the 'active ingredients' in each and its mass in one tablet. They also worked out the cost of ten tablets and did an experiment to measure the volume of hydrochloric acid needed to neutralize one tablet of each brand. Their results were:

Brand	Active ingredient	Mass of active ingredient in each tablet	Cost of 10 tablets	Volume of acid to neutralize
Brand **A**	aluminium hydroxide	80 mg*	50 p	30 cm^3
Brand **B**	magnesium hydroxide	60 mg	40 p	20 cm^3
Brand **C**	sodium hydrogencarbonate	90 mg	30 p	10 cm^3

*1 mg (milligram) is 0.001 g.

a Why was it a useful test of the tablets to see how much acid was needed to neutralize each one?
b Which brand gives the greatest mass of active ingredient per penny? Explain your answer.
c Which brand neutralizes the most acid per penny? Explain your answer.
d Which would you rate the 'best buy' *on the given information*?
e What other tests would you do if you were trying to work out which was the best buy?
f Describe (with full practical details) how you would measure the amount of acid needed to neutralize a tablet.

Chapter 7   **Water**

7.1 The water cycle

Almost all of the water on the earth is found in the seas and oceans and the rest of it is moving round in a **cycle** (Fig 7.1).

When the sea warms up, some of the water evaporates (Chapter 1); the water vapour is carried upwards by convection (*Physics 11–14*, Chapter 24). As it goes up, it encounters colder and colder conditions and the vapour condenses to a liquid and often freezes to a solid. We see the result as clouds. As conditions change and the droplets or ice particles get larger, they start to fall to the earth as snow, hail or, more often, rain. Most of the rain falls back into the sea but some falls on land.

Water is an excellent solvent (Chapter 1) for many substances and on its way down the rain dissolves gases such as carbon dioxide and oxygen that are present in the air. It is the oxygen dissolved in the water that enables fish to live. When the water falls on the land it makes its way to the sea via streams and rivers. Sometimes it forms lakes or moves underground. It will, of course, dissolve any soluble rocks (salts) and these find their way into the sea, which has become very salty indeed. If the stream or river flows rapidly, insoluble solids are also carried

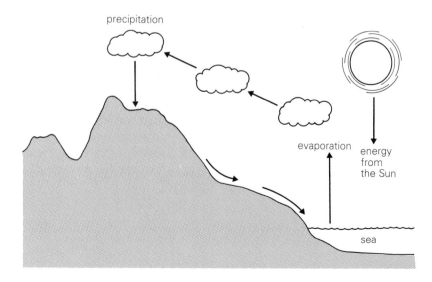

Fig 7.1 The water cycle.

along. A river can cut deep or wide valleys through the landscape and can leave caves if it meets soluble rock. Streams which have passed through limestone country have calcium salts dissolved in them and the water is said to be 'hard' (see Chapter 9).

Background Reading

Acid rain

As the rain falls through the air it dissolves some of the gases – oxygen and carbon dioxide. Since carbon dioxide is acidic, it follows that rainwater will be acidic. But carbon dioxide is only *weakly* acidic and so normal rain has a pH of 5 or 6, which does little harm, but if the atmosphere is polluted with sulphur dioxide from power stations and nitrogen dioxide from vehicle exhausts (Chapter 4), then the rain becomes much more acidic and the pH falls to 4 or even lower. Such rain can be very harmful and can cause much damage to buildings and statues (Fig 7.2) if they are made out of limestone or marble (Chapter 9). In addition, the pH of rivers and lakes falls so low that life becomes impossible and all the plants and fish die (*Biology 11–14* Chapter 20). In this case the acid rain may not be the only cause since pine forests also produce acid decay products if the trees are planted too close together. The forests of Scandinavia are suffering as a result of acid rain said to have come partly from Britain.

To cure the problems caused by acid rain by using neutralization is almost impossible. As is often the case,

Fig 7.2 The effect of acid rain.

prevention is better than cure and the only answer is to avoid producing the very acidic gases in the first place. This can be done by treating the gases from power stations to remove sulphur dioxide and the gases from vehicle exhausts to remove nitrogen dioxide. These are expensive processes and we would have to pay more for electricity and transport if this were done.

Questions
1 Why do power stations produce sulphur dioxide?
2 Why do vehicle exhaust fumes contain nitrogen dioxide?
3 Why are these gases dangerous?
   (See Chapter 4, page 45)

7.2 Water purification

The water returning to the sea can be made to make a detour – it can be piped into our homes (or factories) from lakes, rivers or underground sources. Before it comes out of our taps it passes through a water treatment plant (Fig 7.3) where the following things happen to it:

Fig 7.3 A water treatment plant.

a It is filtered to remove large particles.

Table 7.1 Use of water in the home.

Use	Volume used per person per day (litres)
flushing lavatories	40
washing ourselves	37
washing clothes	20
washing dishes and cleaning	12
cooking and drinking	6
other uses	5

b It is allowed to settle to get rid of smaller particles (alum is sometimes added to speed up this process).

c It is then chemically treated – the most important process being adding chlorine to kill all the micro-organisms which are present.

d If necessary the pH is adjusted with lime (see Chapter 6) to ensure that it is close to neutral. If it is too acid or too alkaline it will react with metal pipes and tanks.

Our water sometimes smells very slightly of chlorine but that is the price we pay for controlling killer diseases. In the nineteenth century impure water caused many thousands to die of cholera and typhoid.

In different parts of the country water tastes different. This is because different salts are dissolved in it. However, not much of our water is drunk. Table 7.1 shows how we use it in our homes.

When we have finished with our water it has to be returned to the river or sea. It is very impure and it is often referred to as sewage. One of the most disgraceful scandals in Britain is the way that so much sewage is pumped untreated out to sea and into rivers with disastrous consequences for the biological life of the area. Sewage can be treated and pure water returned to the rivers or the sea. This is done in a sewage treatment plant (Fig 7.4).

Fig 7.4 A sewage treatment plant.

Chemical analysts are involved at all times measuring the purity of water in rivers, in water mains and in the outflow from sewage works. They test for:

a amount of oxygen dissolved

b pH

c soluble salts such as phosphate and nitrate

d solid residues.

7.3 Water pollution

A well balanced river or stream contains bacteria which can remove small quantities of natural pollutants, such as the waste products of animals. However, water becomes polluted when there is too much:

a industrial waste (which is poisonous to river life)

b detergent – from washing clothes and dishes

c fertilizer – washed off land by rainwater

d untreated sewage.

Detergents and fertilizers encourage the growth of some plants and bacteria. This causes such a frenzied amount of activity that the oxygen dissolved in the water is all used up and fish die.

In the last twenty years, however, the state of pollution in some of Britain's rivers has been improving. Chemists have identified the problem and both industry and government have worked to clean up certain rivers. Salmon now swim up the Thames which thirty years ago resembled a large sewer. However, at the same time other rivers have become much more polluted. We have done part of the job; we must now finish it.

7.4 Rusting

Steel (a form of iron) is one of the cheapest and most useful metals, but its greatest disadvantage is the fact that it reacts with the gases of the air to form rust. Chemists need to know as much as possible about the process of rusting so they can try to prevent it.

Which parts of the air cause rusting? From our experience we might well suggest that oxygen is involved. If the experiment shown in Fig 7.5 is set up and left for several days, it is found that about $\frac{1}{5}$ of the air has been used up. The gas remaining in the tube puts out a lighted splint. Therefore oxygen is involved when iron rusts.

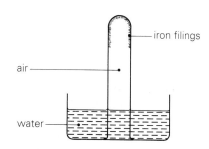

Fig 7.5 The rusting of iron.

Experiment 7.1
Investigating the rusting of iron

1 Put four clean test-tubes in a rack and label them A, B, C and D. Place an iron nail in each.

2 Add distilled water to tube A (damp air) so that about a quarter of the nail shows above the surface.

3 Add a similar volume of salt solution to tube B (damp, salty air).

4 Place a spatula measure of anhydrous calcium chloride in tube C (dry air) and seal tightly with a rubber bung. The anhydrous calcium chloride is a drying agent which will remove all the water vapour from the air in the test-tube.

Safety note

Anhydrous calcium chloride is irritant

5 Boil 5 cm depth of distilled water in a beaker with a few antibumping granules.

6 Fill tube D (water but no air) to well above the top of the nail with the boiled distilled water. Then add a small amount of oil to float on the surface to keep out the air.

7 Place the test-tubes in a safe place and leave them for a week.

8 After a week examine each of the test-tubes and record your results.

Only the iron in tubes A and B rusts (Fig 7.6). So we can say that oxygen *and* water are necessary for iron to rust. More rust is formed in tube B than in tube A.

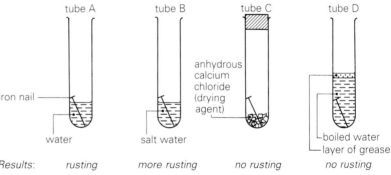

Fig 7.6 Investigating the rusting of iron.

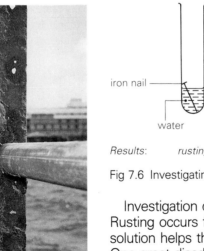

Fig 7.7 Rusting (upright) and galvanized (horizontal) iron in a fence.

Investigation of rust shows that it is hydrated iron oxide. Rusting occurs faster if salt is present. This is because salt solution helps the water to conduct electricity (see Chapter 13). One great disadvantage of putting salt on the roads in winter is that the steel bodies of cars rust much more quickly when the salty water splashes on them.

The prevention of rusting is a problem which has not been completely solved. Methods of keeping air and moisture away from iron by painting or by turning the surface into iron phosphate are reasonably good. Galvanizing (covering the iron with a layer of zinc) is better as it prevents rusting (even at scratches) by an electrical effect.

Summary

1 In the water cycle, water evaporates from seas and lakes to fall again as rain.

2 In water treatment plants, river water is filtered and chemically treated to make it fit to drink.

3 In sewage works the sewage is filtered and then cleaned by the action of bacteria.

4 Water can be polluted by domestic and industrial waste, detergents, fertilizers and sewage.

5 Water and air (oxygen) are needed for iron to rust. Salt solution speeds up the process.

Questions

1 Redraw the water cycle (Fig 7.1) to show what happens when men and animals get involved.

2 Explain why the sea is salty.

3 'Water is a landscaping agent.' Describe what this means.

4 Give one word in each case to describe:
  a the process by which water in the sea becomes water vapour in the air.
  b the process by which water in clouds becomes water in lakes or rivers.
  c the process by which large particles are removed from river water in a water treatment plant.
  d the things which act on sewage in a sewage treatment plant to stop it being harmful.
  e the gas which gets used up when fertilizers pollute a river.

5 You move into a house which has a pond and a stream in the garden. You take some of the water from the pond and the stream into school.
  a How would you compare:
    (i) The amount of dissolved solid in stream and pond water.
    (ii) The amount of insoluble solid in each.
  b Do these results tell you whether the water is fit to drink? Explain your answer.

6 Look at the data in Table 7.1.
  a Draw this as a pie chart.
  b How much of the water which we use really needs to be 'fit to drink' and how much could be of lower quality?
  c Would it be worth having two supplies of water to each house, one of drinking water, the other of a lower standard?

7 In old houses the waste-pipes from the roof drain into the sewers. In newer houses they run into the same pipes as the road-drains. Why do you think that this change was made?

8 Here is part of an article from a local newspaper:

KILLER GAS IN WATER SUPPLY!
Yes, the poison gas chlorine, used on our gallant lads in the First World War comes out of your taps. This was grudgingly admitted to our sharp-questioning reporter by Mr Bouquet the Environmental Health Officer who is in charge of our new waterworks. He claims that chlorine is necessary in the water now that it comes from the river, not boreholes. This paper says 'How can any poison be good for us?' ...

Write a letter to the paper explaining why chlorine is necessary and how it is not harmful in these conditions.

9 Imagine you are the director of a large sewage works giving a talk at a meeting of residents who live near your works. Think what their likely objections might be. Write a speech which deals with these objections and says how useful the sewage works is to the community.

10 What experiment would you carry out to prove that nitrogen and water together do not cause rusting?

11 a In what ways are burning, breathing and rusting similar?
b How does rusting differ from burning and breathing?

12 Three students are talking about rusting. Each makes one of the following remarks:
a All kinds of iron rust.
b Galvanised iron (iron covered by a layer of zinc) doesn't rust.
c Dry iron doesn't rust.
Write instructions for experiments to find out which students are right and which are wrong. You get marks for planning the experiments, not for knowing the correct answers.

13 'Rusting is wasteful and expensive.' Explain what this means.

Chapter 8   The chemical elements

8.1 Elements and compounds

We first met the term element in Chapter 4 when we were
looking at substances which burned in air. You will remember
that an element, when it burns, gives a single oxide. This ties in
with the definition of an element as a substance which cannot be
broken down into anything simpler by chemical means. Some
naturally occurring substances, such as nitrogen, oxygen and gold,
are elements. Other elements, such as copper, can be extracted
from their compounds fairly easily; while metals such as sodium
and potassium can be obtained only with difficulty. In all there are
ninety naturally occurring elements. Since 1940 man has
managed to make another fifteen, all of which are dangerously
radioactive. Of the ninety, less than forty are common enough to
be met outside universities.

Any single substance which is not an element is a compound.
A compound can be defined as a substance consisting of two or
more elements chemically combined together. In Chapter 4 we
found that when compounds burn they usually give a mixture of
the oxides of the elements which they contain. In Chapter 5 we
learned more about compounds and saw how they differed from
mixtures of elements. Thus *definite amounts* of the elements
zinc and sulphur combine together in a *chemical reaction* to form
the compound zinc sulphide. A mixture of zinc and sulphur
remains a mixture of elements rather than a compound.

The names of compounds often show which elements they
contain. For example, copper sulph*ide* contains copper and
sulphur, chemically combined together. The ending -*ide* means
that only sulphur is present with copper, but the ending -*ate*
means that oxygen is also present. Thus copper sulphate means
copper, sulphur *and oxygen* chemically combined together.

8.2 Metals and nonmetals

Obviously life would be difficult for chemists if they had to
remember the details of 100 elements and their compounds.

Fortunately several elements often resemble each other and behave in the same way, so it is possible to classify the elements into large sets, and then divide them into subsets. Thus it is possible to forecast how an element will behave if we know which set it is in. The first division involves classifying the elements into two sets, the metals and the nonmetals.

8.3 Physical properties of the elements

Metallic elements can often be recognized because they shine brightly at a freshly cut or scraped surface. They can also be hammered into different shapes without breaking and are said to be **malleable**. Blacksmiths, silversmiths and goldsmiths all make use of this property of malleability of the metals with which they work. Nonmetals by contrast are **brittle**.

Another way of recognizing a metal is that it will conduct electricity very well. This can be seen by using the apparatus in Fig 8.1. Not only do metals conduct electricity well, but they are also good conductors of energy, as you will know if you have ever tried to touch the handle of a poker which has been left in a fire. (See *Physics 11–14* page 242.)

Most nonmetals are poor conductors of energy and electricity, but there is one exception. One of the forms of the element carbon, called graphite, is a fairly good conductor of electricity, though the other form of carbon (diamond) is a bad conductor like all the other nonmetallic elements.

Measurement of melting point is not a good way of distinguishing metals from nonmetals. Most metals have a higher melting point than most nonmetals, but there are exceptions. Carbon and some other nonmetals have very high melting points, while metals such as sodium melt at low temperatures (see Table 8.1 overleaf). However, it is possible to say that if an element is a gas at room temperature it must be a nonmetal. There are only two elements which are liquids at room temperature – bromine (a nonmetal) and mercury (a metal).

The densities of metals vary widely and it is helpful here to divide the set of metals into two subsets: 'reactive metals' and 'everyday metals'. We meet 'reactive metals' (sodium, calcium, etc.) as elements only in the laboratory, since they are too reactive to be used to make common articles. However, we are familiar with objects made from copper, iron, etc., so these are termed 'everyday metals'. It is found that 'everyday metals' have a higher density than nonmetals but 'reactive metals' are less dense than many nonmetals (see Table 8.1).

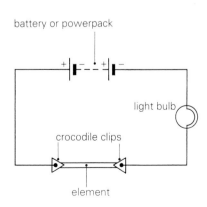

Fig 8.1 Testing the conductivity of an element.

Table 8.1 The properties of some elements.

Element	Type	Melting point (°C)	Density (g per cm^3)	Nature of oxide	Solubility of oxide	pH of oxide solution
carbon	nonmetal	very high	2.2	gas	fairly soluble	4.5
hydrogen	nonmetal	−259	0.00008	liquid	soluble	7
phosphorus	nonmetal	44	1.8	solid – low melting point	very soluble – violent reaction	0
sulphur	nonmetal	113	2.1	gas	soluble	1
copper	everyday metal	1080	8.9	black solid	insoluble	
iron	everyday metal	1540	7.9	black or brown solid	insoluble	
lead	everyday metal	327	11.4	yellow, red or brown solid	insoluble	
zinc	everyday metal	419	7.1	white solid (yellow when hot)	insoluble	
calcium	reactive metal	850	1.6	white solid	fairly soluble	12
magnesium	reactive metal	650	1.7	white solid	sparingly soluble	9
potassium	reactive metal	64	0.9	white solid	very soluble	14
sodium	reactive metal	98	1.0	white solid	very soluble	14

Background Reading

Three important metals: aluminium, copper and iron

Being 'everyday' metals we meet these three often in our everyday lives. As they are metals, they are all strong, malleable and good conductors. (Thus all three are used for different kinds of cooking pans.) Iron is not normally found on its own but in steel (an alloy of iron and carbon). Steel's malleability varies with the amount of carbon it contains (see Section 11.4). Other properties of the three metals are shown below:

	Aluminium (Al)	Copper (Cu)	Iron (Fe)
melting point (°C)	660	1080	1540
density (g/cm^3)	2.7	8.9	7.9
cost per tonne (1991)	£1550	£1300	£200
corrosion	reactive, but a layer of aluminium oxide forms which protects the surface	unreactive, so corrodes very slowly	rusts easily
electrical conductivity	very good	very good	fair

You will see that aluminium has a much lower melting point than the other two, though this does not affect many of its uses. Its main advantage is its 'lightness', so it is used particularly where a low-density metal is needed.

Iron's main advantage over the others is that it is considerably cheaper, so it is used where price is very important. It can also be made much harder than the other two.

Copper's advantage is its lack of corrosion, so it is used for roofing and coins. Like aluminium, it is a good conductor of electricity.

	Aluminium	Copper	Iron
main advantage	low density	does not corrode	cheap
main disadvantage	expensive	expensive	rusts easily
uses	power lines aeroplanes ships	electrical wiring roofing pipes machinery	car bodies rails hammers machine tools

Questions
1 State, giving your reasons, which of the three metals you would suggest using for:
 a a lorry engine
 b a hang-glider
 c connecting lengths of hosepipe
 d a new paper fastener.

2 The following uses of copper are given in a data book:
 electrical wiring 58%
 roofing material, pipes 19%
 machinery 17%
 other uses 6%
 draw a pie chart to illustrate this.

8.4 The oxides of elements

We saw in Chapter 4 that many substances react with oxygen, and that the behaviour of their oxides provides another way of distinguishing between metals and nonmetals. The first difference is that the oxides of nonmetals usually have low melting and boiling points, so they are either gases, liquids or volatile solids at room temperature. Metal oxides all have high melting and boiling points.

The other way of distinguishing between metal and nonmetal oxides is by finding out if they are acids or bases (Chapter 6).

Nonmetal oxides dissolve in water to give a pH which is less than 7, that is they are acidic. Metal oxides are bases – they

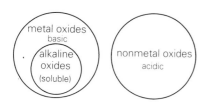

Fig 8.2 The oxides of the elements.

neutralize acids to form salts. Copper oxide is insoluble in water and so, although it is a base, it is not an alkali. In general the metals that we meet in everyday life are those which form insoluble basic oxides and these oxides are often coloured. It is the reactive metals which form oxides which produce alkaline solutions, as Table 8.1 shows. Thus we can say that:

most nonmetals form oxides which have low melting points and are acidic;

most metals form oxides which have high melting points and are basic, some also being alkaline.

This is illustrated by the Venn diagram shown in Fig 8.2.

8.5 Atoms and molecules

At the beginning of the nineteenth century, John Dalton developed an idea that had been suggested by the ancient Greeks. This was that matter consisted of tiny particles. This idea of small particles is needed to understand the kinetic theory (*Physics 11–14*, page 106).

The smallest particles of elements are called **atoms**. All the atoms of one element have the same chemical properties. When elements combine to form compounds, their atoms join together in some way. *One* way in which they can do this is to form **molecules**, which are small groups of atoms chemically bound together. A molecule of water, with the formula H_2O, has two atoms of hydrogen combined with one atom of oxygen. On paper it can be written as $H\diagup\overset{O}{}\diagdown H$ but its shape is better shown by a model as in Fig 8.3. This figure also shows some other models of molecules. You will see that both elements and compounds can consist of molecules though a molecule of a compound consists of more than one type of atom.

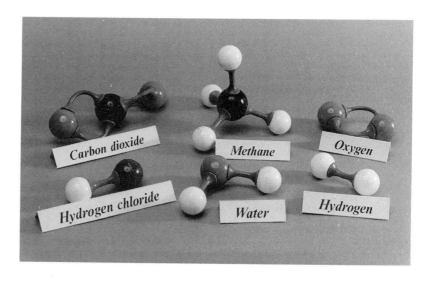

Fig 8.3 Models of simple molecules.

Background Reading

Which material?

There are lots of elements and compounds but only a few of them are suitable for making everyday materials. Five classes into which materials are often divided are: **metals, ceramics, glass, plastics** and **fibres**. We have already dealt with metals in this chapter and ceramics are commonly met as 'china' in the kitchen and dining-room. Glass and its uses are well known (see also in Section 9.5). Fibres include natural fibres like wool and cotton as well as man-made fibres (such as nylon and Terylene). The word 'plastic' is used to cover a large group of materials, all of which are compounds which mostly contain carbon and hydrogen (and sometimes other elements). You will discover in your later study of chemistry that there are many kinds of plastics and that they do not all have the same properties. However, they have a lot in common and they are increasingly being used to replace other materials.

In deciding which material to use to make a particular object, it is necessary to know the properties of the materials we have mentioned. These are summarised in the table below:

	Metals	Plastics	Ceramics	Glass	Fibres
Density	often high	low	low	low	low
Strength when bent	difficult to bend but then bend without snapping	flexible but can snap or split	snap	snap	strong
Hardness when scratched	hard	soft	hard	hard	soft
Behaviour when pulled	strong	distort	break	break	strong
Effect of heating	high melting point	soften easily – thus readily moulded	very high melting point	quite high melting point	soften or burn
Conduction of heat and electricity	good	poor	poor	poor	poor
Corrosion	tend to corrode	←———— very little tendency to corrode ————→			
Cost	high	variable	low	low	variable

Plastics are used as alternatives to metals where low density, cheapness and lack of corrosion are important and as alternatives to ceramics and glass when flexibility is required. Metals are used particularly when strength or good conductivity are required.

Questions

1 These objects are made of either plastic or metal. Discuss each one, saying when you would use metal and when plastic:
  a Buckets   **b** Combs   **c** Rulers

2 In how many of the materials shown in the table could the following be made? Give a situation in which each material would be most suitable:
  a Drinking vessels   **d** Storage jars
  b Spoons   **e** Strong crane cable
  c Windows   **f** Furnace lining

Summary

We have seen that pure substances can first be divided into elements and compounds. Elements can be divided into metals and nonmetals, and metals can be divided into 'everyday' and 'reactive' metals. This can be summed up in a diagram (Fig 8.4).

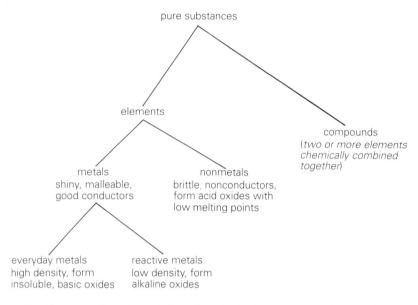

pure substances

elements

compounds
(*two or more elements chemically combined together*)

metals
shiny, malleable, good conductors

nonmetals
brittle, nonconductors, form acid oxides with low melting points

everyday metals
high density, form insoluble, basic oxides

reactive metals
low density, form alkaline oxides

Fig 8.4 A summary of Chapter 8.

Further classification of the chemical elements can be made; this leads to the Periodic Table (see Chapter 15).

Background Reading

The discovery and naming of the elements

The Ancient Greeks thought that all matter was composed of four elements – earth, air, fire and water. The medieval alchemists held similar views and it was not until the eighteenth century that the elements we know today were recognized as such. Even so, a number of metallic elements were known in classical times, although they were not thought to be elements. Some were also associated in earlier times with particular planets (Table 8.2).

Chemical symbols reflect chemical names and are usually of two letters, though sometimes only one letter is used. The first letter is always large and the second letter always small. As can be seen in Table 8.2, the symbols follow the classical rather than the English names.

Most of the other symbols follow naturally from the English names, but there are some exceptions. The symbol for potassium is K and comes from the Arabic name, 'kalium'. Potassium is still known as kalium in many other languages, just as sodium is known as 'natrium', which accounts for its symbol, Na. The symbol of the element tungsten, W, derives from 'wolfram'.

Table 8.2 Some elements known in classical times.

English name	Symbol	Classical name	Planet
gold	Au	aurum	(Sun)
silver	Ag	argentum	(Moon)
mercury	Hg	hydrargyrum	Mercury
copper	Cu	cuprum	Venus
iron	Fe	ferrum	Mars
tin	Sn	stannum	Jupiter
lead	Pb	plumbum	Saturn
antimony	Sb	stibium	

In addition to the classical elements, some other elements are named after planets, for example uranium (U), plutonium (Pu) and neptunium (Np). These all end -*ium*, an ending common to the more recently discovered metals. Not all elements are named after planets; some are named after places on earth which can vary from small villages, where the element was first found, to vast continents (Table 8.3).

Table 8.3 Some elements which are named after places.

Element	Symbol	Origin
strontium	Sr	Strontian, a Scottish village
holmium	Ho	Stockholm, a city
germanium	Ge	Germany, a country
europium	Eu	Europe, a continent

Others are named after people (for example, Cm, 'curium' after Marie Curie) or after colours (Cl, chlorine from the Greek word for green). The use of Greek is very common in naming the elements and other examples include hydrogen, H (water former); neon, Ne (new) and bromine, Br (stench).

After classical times, few elements were discovered until the last third of the eighteenth century when a number of nonmetals and everyday metals were first made. The discovery of electrolysis (Chapter 13) enabled Humphry Davy to make the reactive metals for the first time in 1807 and 1808. Throughout the nineteenth century new elements continued to be discovered and the last nonradioactive element, rhenium, was not discovered until 1925. One of the oddest discoveries was that of the gas helium, which was first discovered on the sun in 1868 (the Greek for sun is helios). It was not until 1895 that it was first isolated on earth by the British scientists Ramsey and Travers, who were preparing all the noble gases for the first time.

Since the application of 'nuclear techniques' in 1940, fifteen new radioactive elements have been made by man, and it is not at all certain how many more new elements will be produced in future. It is unlikely to be a great number, for many of these new elements decompose very rapidly into lighter elements as soon as they are made (Table 8.4).

Table 8.4 The number of elements known at various dates.

Year	200	1700	1750	1800	1850	1900	1950	2000
Number of elements known	about 10	14	16	33	59	84	97	?

Questions
1 Use a dictionary to try to find out the origins of the following names:
   a Carbon.
   b Chromium.
   c Lithium.
   d Rubidium.

2 After which places are the following named?
   a Am **b** Cf **c** Po **d** Sc **e** Ga and Fr.

3 Carbon – C, oxygen – O, potassium – P, sodium – S, uranium – U.
   a Which of the symbols are incorrect?
   b For each element with an incorrect symbol, supply the correct symbol.
   c For each symbol with an incorrect element, supply the correct element.

4 Draw a bar chart to show the number of elements discovered between 1700 and 1750, between 1750 and 1800 and so on.

Questions

1 a What is meant by a chemical element?
   b What is a chemical compound?
   c How does a mixture of hydrogen and oxygen differ from the compound water (hydrogen hydroxide)?

2 Single pure chemical substances may be either elements or compounds. Elements may be either metals or nonmetals. Divide the following six substances into:
   a Metallic elements.
   b Nonmetallic elements.
   c Compounds.
   Calcium, carbon, copper sulphate, mercury, nitrogen, water.

3 Everyday substances around us are either elements, compounds or mixtures. Give one example of each of these and state in each case why you believe it belongs to that group.

4 Choose from the following list of substances:
  a An element.
  b A solid compound.
  c A mixture.
  d An acidic oxide.
  e A solid conductor of electricity.
  f A neutral oxide.
  Carbon dioxide, copper, propanone, copper sulphate, sea water, magnesium oxide, oxygen, pure water, sulphur, air.

5 a (i) What have copper, iron, sulphur and tin in common?
    (ii) How does sulphur differ from the other members of the group?
  b (i) What have carbon dioxide, iron oxide, sulphur dioxide and water in common?
    (ii) In what way does iron oxide differ from the other members of the group?

6 A student found a lump of a yellow mineral which he thought was either sulphur or gold.
  a What can he deduce from the following experimental results?
    It did not conduct electricity.
    It did not melt when heated with a Bunsen burner.
    It did not catch fire when heated in air.
  b Could the mineral be either sulphur or gold?

7 Describe two differences (other than colour) which you would expect to find between a cylinder of copper metal and a roll of sulphur which are exactly the same size and shape.

8 Classify the following elements as reactive metals, everyday metals or nonmetals. Give your reasons.
  a A gas, A, which burns to give a liquid oxide, pH 7.
  b A gas, B, which forms no oxide.
  c A liquid, C, which conducts electricity well and forms a red insoluble oxide.
  d A solid, D, which is very shiny and which forms a black insoluble oxide.
  e A solid, E, which reacts rapidly in air to form a whitish oxide that is very soluble (pH 14).
  f A black solid, F, which is a good conductor of electricity and burns to give a soluble gaseous oxide (pH 4.5).
  g A solid, G, which is a poor conductor of electricity and which forms a very soluble white acidic oxide.
  h A shiny solid, H, which is a good conductor but is chemically not very reactive.
    If you can, deduce the names of the elements A, C and F.

9 Study carefully the properties of the substances recorded in the table below.

Substance	Electrical conductivity	What happens when heated in air
A	good	becomes coated with film of oxide
B	none	burns to give carbon dioxide and water
C	good	burns very vigorously
D	none	melts and burns with a blue flame
E	fair	glows red hot and produces a gas that turns limewater milky

a Which of the substances A–E is a compound? Give a reason for your answer.
b Which two of the substances are metallic elements? Which is the more reactive?
c Suggest a name for one of these two metallic elements, giving the letter of the substance you are naming.
d Suggest what the element D might be.
e What is substance E?

10 State, giving your reasons, whether you think that the lettered substances are elements, compounds or mixtures.
a W burned readily to give water and a gas that turned limewater milky.
b X melted over a wide range of temperature: on further heating, its boiling point gradually rose as it was distilled.
c Y melted sharply at 337 °C and then gave off a gas which rekindled a glowing splint.
d Z melted sharply and then burned to give only one oxide.

11 The table below gives information about six actual elements which are disguised by the letters A–F. State which letter in the table refers to:
a Copper.   **c** Oxygen.
b Mercury.   **d** Sodium.
Give your reasons in each case.

Element	Melting point (°C)	Does it conduct electricity?	Does it catch fire when heated in air?
A	−259	no	yes
B	−39	yes	no
C	98	yes	yes
D	−219	no	no
E	1083	yes	no
F	119	no	yes

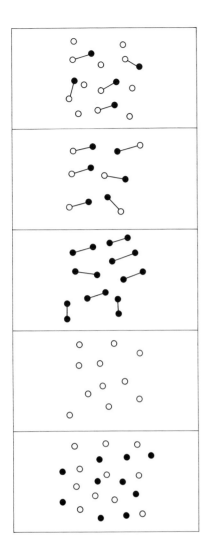

Fig 8.5.

12 In each of the following cases, name an *element* which, when heated in air:
  a Burns with a brilliant flame and leaves a white ash.
  b Melts easily and burns with a blue flame, producing a choking gas.
  c Glows red and produces a gas which turns limewater milky.

13 Here is a list of some chemical elements.
  Argon, calcium, carbon, chlorine, copper, hydrogen, iron, nitrogen, oxygen, sodium, sulphur, zinc.
  The question is about pairs of these elements:
  a Which two combine to make water?
  b Which two are the commonest gases in the atmosphere?
  c Which two are solid nonmetals?
  d Which two are metals whose oxides form alkaline solutions?
  e Name two from the list which combine to make a sharp-smelling, choking gas.
  f Name two metals from the list which might be found in and around your home.

14 Use Appendix 1 on page 173 to make a list of five elements in each case which obey the following rules:
  a Everyday metals melt above 600 °C.
  b Nonmetals have densities less than 3.0 g/cm^3.
  c Metals names end in -ium.

15 List the *exceptions* to the rules in the previous question.

16 In the diagrams (Fig 8.5) the black circles represent one sort of atom and the white circles a different sort of atom.
  Which diagram corresponds to:
  a An element which exists as single atoms.
  b A compound.
  c An element which exists as molecules.
  d A mixture of an element and a compound.

Chapter 9   **Rocks**

9.1 The Earth

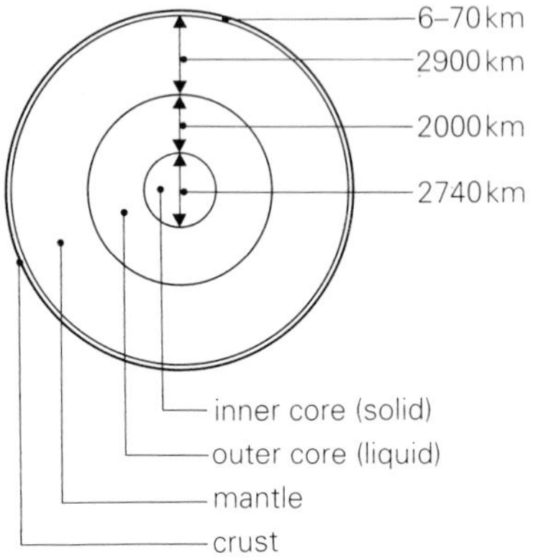

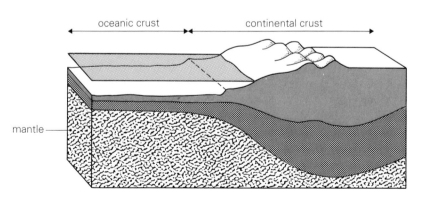

6–70 km
2900 km
2000 km
2740 km

inner core (solid)
outer core (liquid)
mantle
crust

Fig 9.1 Section through the Earth.

It is now thought that the Earth was formed 4500 million years ago, the various chemical elements being present in almost the same proportions as they are today. Radioactive elements, such as uranium, have decayed and the rate of this decay has helped us to estimate the age of the Earth. Changes that happen on the Earth do so very slowly but by studying the rocks, fossils in the rocks and what is happening at the moment, scientists have gradually built up a picture of how the Earth reached its present state.

The circumference of the Earth is about 40 000 kilometres and the radius is about 6300 kilometres. The Earth is not uniform and is made of three distinct parts (Fig 9.1). The **core** at the centre is partly solid and partly liquid and is mainly iron. It is believed that the Earth's magnetic field is caused by the liquid core. The **mantle** is solid, except where the rock has been melted by the high temperature of the core. Molten rock, called **magma**, can escape during volcanic eruptions.

The **crust** above the mantle varies in thickness: the crust under the oceans is thin (about 6 km), whereas the continental crust averages 35 km, though it may be as much as 70 km under mountain ranges (Fig 9.2).

oceanic crust   continental crust

mantle

Fig 9.2 Mantle and crust.

The crust consists of a series of **plates** floating on the mantle. The crust has a lower density than the mantle so the plates float much like pack ice. The major plates are shown in Fig 9.3. They only move a few tens of kilometres in a million years – but

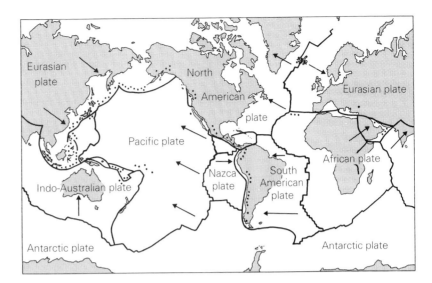

Fig 9.3 The Plates (dots indicate main earthquake areas).

these movements account for mountain building and other changes:

Mountains form where plates collide.
Oceans develop as the plates separate.
Earthquakes occur where plates meet and grind together.
(The dots on Fig 9.3 show earthquake zones.)
When one plate is pushed beneath another, the lower rock melts because of the high temperature generated and often pushes to the surface as volcanoes (Fig 9.4).

It is important to remember that the Earth is a restless planet constantly undergoing change – though the time scale is very long.

Fig 9.4 Volcano formation.

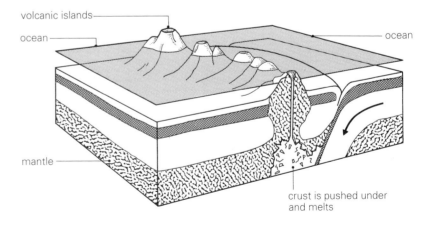

9.2 The origin of rocks and minerals

Molten rock which emerges through volcanoes is called **lava**. As this cools it forms a variety of solids and these are known as

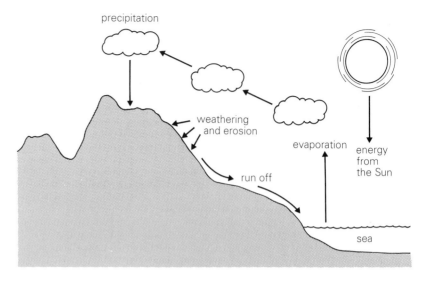

Fig 9.5 The water cycle.

igneous rocks (from the Latin for 'fire') — one example is granite. A great many elements are present as very complicated compounds in such rocks but the two commonest are silicon and oxygen. Some valuable minerals form among the less valuable rocks when they crystallize from the molten magma.

Over long periods of time, igneous rocks are weathered by the wind and rain (Fig 9.5) and are broken down into very small grains. These grains are washed from the land into seas or lakes where they sink to the bottom. This is called **deposition** and the deposits are called sediments. The rocks that form when these sediments are closely packed together are called **sedimentary rocks.** The individual grains can often be seen by the naked eye or a microscope, whereas igneous rocks are crystalline (Fig 9.6).

The two most common sedimentary rocks are sandstones and limestone. Sandstones are mainly made up of sand (silicon

Fig 9.6 Examples of crystalline igneous rocks.

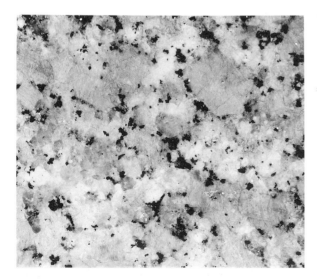

(a) Granite

(b) sandstone.

oxide) which is white but many other oxides can also be present. For example, red sandstones contain a lot of iron oxide. Limestones will be investigated in Section 9.4. Because of the way they are formed, sedimentary rocks are not pure and most sandstones contain a little limestone and most limestones contain a little silicon oxide.

A third class of rocks are known as **metamorphic**. These rocks, like igneous rocks, are crystalline and form when other rocks are subjected to conditions such as heat or pressure which alter them (Fig 9.7). Marble and slate are examples of metamorphic rocks.

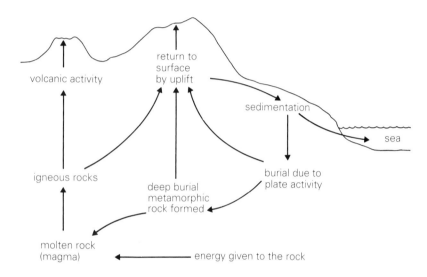

Fig 9.7 The rock cycle.

Less common, but of more interest, is a set of minerals called **evaporite minerals.** As the name implies, these are formed from a solution (lake or sea) when the water evaporates. They then crystallize, the least soluble forming first. This is how the enormous sodium chloride deposits were formed under parts of Britain.

9.3 Soil

When rocks are weathered, but the grains are not washed into the sea, they go to make up one of man's most valuable possessions – **soil.** Soils are often known by names which betray their rocky origins, sandy or chalky for example. But soils are very complicated mixtures and contain much else, including humus (see *Biology 11–14*, page 146) and water. Growing plants use many of the soil's chemical elements. Farmers therefore replenish the soil by adding various chemical compounds to the fields. Soils can become more acidic with each succeeding crop so that lime has to be applied to increase the pH (Section 6.4).

Background Reading

Quarrying and the environment

Limestone and sandstone are sedimentary rocks which are plentiful and found near the surface in this country. The topsoil is scraped away and the mineral is dug out, sometimes after being loosened by blasting. Sand and gravel are other sediments which are even easier to get at.

The value of the minerals is quite low since they are readily available and easily extracted. Thus they are usually mined close to where they will be used – limestone near a chemical works and sand and gravel all over the country as they are used for building. Otherwise transport costs could be greater than the worth of the mineral.

Quarrying, while necessary, is most unsightly and scars the landscape. Limestone rocks form some of the most beautiful scenery in the country (for example the Mendip Hills or the Yorkshire Dales). Hence there is an outcry when a proposal is made to set up a quarry in such a place. Against the inconvenience to local people and the damage to the environment must be set the dependence of our quality of life on limestone, sand and gravel.

Fig 9.8 A limestone quarry in North Yorkshire.

However, the quarrying firms must be sensitive to the feelings of those living near the quarry and reduce its impact by careful landscaping. Once all the mineral has been extracted, the landscaping must continue. Topsoil can be put back and the quarry grassed over or the quarry can be landscaped into a lake, as is often done with gravel pits.

Questions

1 How would *your* quality of life be affected if no more limestone were quarried?

2 Imagine a quarrying company Caldig wanted to open a limestone quarry in the beautiful Mendip Hills. You are a television reporter interviewing a local resident (who is against the mining) and a spokesperson for the company (who is for the mining). Write the speeches that each might make.

9.4 Limestone

Limestone is a very common sedimentary rock. Tests on powdered limestone give the following results:

Appearance – a white powder.
Effect of heating – no apparent reaction.
Solubility – insoluble in water.
Action of dilute hydrochloric acid – fizzing seen, carbon dioxide is evolved, a colourless solution remains.

The action of acid shows that a carbonate is present. Many carbonates evolve carbon dioxide on heating but the carbonates of the most reactive metals only decompose to give carbon dioxide at high temperatures.

Experiment 9.1
Limestone investigation

1 Suspend a limestone chip from a tripod using some nichrome wire.

2 Heat the chip in the hottest part of a Bunsen flame (just above the blue cone) for a few minutes.

3 Look at the chip and write down what you see.

4 When it has cooled, transfer the chip to a test-tube. Hold the test-tube in your hand and add water, a drop at a time, from a teat pipette. Record all you observe.

5 Shake the chip with more water and filter the suspension you get.

6 Measure the pH of the filtrate with Universal Indicator paper and record your results.

Safety note

Quicklime is corrosive.

7 Using a fresh straw, blow through the filtrate and record what happens.

Optional extras

8 Heat another chip and allow it to cool. Add dilute hydrochloric acid to the heated chip and an unheated chip in separate test-tubes. Compare your results.

9 Add water to a chip which has not been heated. Compare your result with step **4** above.

The residue after heating (step 3) *looks* similar to the limestone you started with but the results from the other steps show that there has been a reaction. The filtrate in step 6 is found to be alkaline so some of the residue must have dissolved. When you blew carbon dioxide through the solution a milkiness appeared.

The solution obviously resembles limewater, which is calcium hydroxide solution. A flame test on any of these solids will give a red flame (see Section 12.3) so we can tell they are calcium compounds.

We can therefore write:

$$\text{calcium carbonate} \xrightarrow{\text{heat}} \text{residue} + \text{carbon dioxide} \xrightarrow{\text{water}} \text{calcium hydroxide}$$
(limestone)

The residue is fairly clearly calcium oxide, since we know that alkaline oxides react with water to form hydroxides (Section 6.3).

A summary of the reactions is shown in Table 9.1. It should be remembered that the milkiness in limewater is calcium carbonate, so that we can go full circle, as shown. Included in the flow diagram are the common names for the materials, and it will be noticed that calcium carbonate occurs in nature not only as limestone, but as marble, chalk, Iceland spar and calcite.

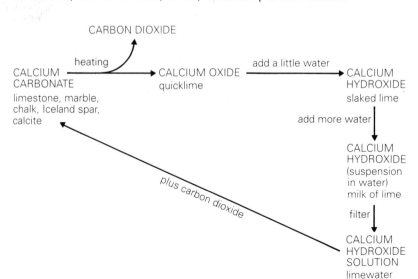

Table 9.1 The reactions of limestone.

9.5 Uses of limestone

Limestone is what is known as a 'free stone': it can easily be cut into blocks and shaped and so is ideal for building. But it does have disadvantages for it is attacked and eaten away by acid rain (Chapter 7) and, being porous, it absorbs water and can then be cracked open by a hard frost (Fig 9.9).

Fig 9.9 Frost damage.

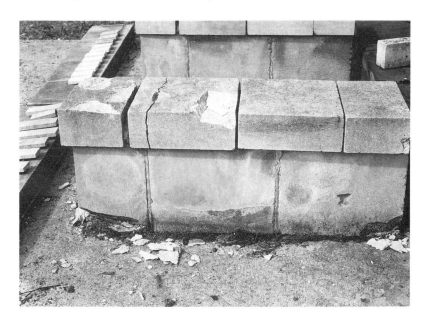

Limestone is also added to the iron ore in iron making (Section 11.4) since it reacts with the impurities to make slag thus preventing the blockage of the furnace with waste products.

A further use for limestone is in the manufacture of glass. Glasses are not proper chemical compounds but are mixtures of oxides. A glass is not crystalline and is transparent. The cheapest glass is made by heating limestone, sodium carbonate and silicon oxide (sand). The temperature used is very high and carbon dioxide is lost and the three oxides (calcium oxide, sodium oxide, and silicon oxide) melt together. The molten mixture can be shaped or blown and then allowed to cool. Other oxides give different properties: boron oxide makes the glass hard, lead oxide makes the glass sparkle and iron oxide makes the glass coloured. It is therefore important to make sure the limestone contains no iron oxide if the end product is to be colourless glass.

When limestone and clay are heated together the result is *cement*. Adding water to cement powder causes a chemical reaction (it gets quite hot) and a hard solid results. If the cement is first mixed with sand and gravel and water is added, the same reaction occurs and *concrete* is produced.

Slaked lime (calcium hydroxide) is used in agriculture to neutralize acid soils (see Chapter 6) and also as an alkali in industry.

9.6 The hardness of water

Water is said to be 'hard' when it does not form a lather (bubbles) with soap. Instead, a white precipitate (called scum) is formed. No lather forms until all the hardness has been removed by the soap and this is a waste of soap. Also the scum tends to grind into clothes when they are being washed, causing damage. Hardness is caused by calcium or magnesium salts dissolved in the water. There are two types of hardness.

Temporary hardness is caused by the presence of calcium hydrogencarbonate or magnesium hydrogencarbonate in solution. It is called temporary because these salts are removed by boiling the water. The hydrogencarbonates get into the water by a reaction which occurs when rainwater flows over limestone rocks. Rainwater contains dissolved carbon dioxide and limestone (calcium carbonate).

The reaction is:

calcium   +   water   +   carbon   ⟶   calcium
carbonate   dioxide   hydrogencarbonate
                                          (soluble)

You can see this reaction occurring if you continue to pass carbon dioxide through calcium hydroxide solution for a long time. The milky precipitate of calcium carbonate which forms at first (Section 9.4) *redissolves* to give calcium hydrogencarbonate and the solution goes clear again.

On boiling the reaction is reversed and carbonates are precipitated. Thus the hardness is removed. However, this is the cause of 'fur' in kettles and scale in boilers and pipes which can be a nuisance. (It can also be dangerous if the pipes become completely blocked.)

Calcium hydrogencarbonate also turns back to calcium carbonate when temporarily hard water is evaporated. This is the cause of stalactites and stalagmites in limestone caves. The water (containing calcium hydrogencarbonate) drips down very slowly and much of it evaporates either at the top (forming a stalactite) or at the bottom (forming a stalagmite). Thus both stalagmites and stalactites are made of calcium carbonate (Fig 9.10).

Permanent hardness is caused by other calcium or magnesium salts, such as sulphates and chlorides. These are present in certain rocks and dissolve in water which passes over them. These salts are not decomposed by boiling.

Water may be softened by several processes, but the commonest is known as 'ion exchange'. Hard water is passed through a water softener which turns the calcium and magnesium salts into sodium salts. These do not cause hardness as they do not form a scum with soap.

Fig 9.10 Stalactites and stalagmites.

A method of measuring hardness is to add soap solution to a water sample in small amounts, shaking after each addition. When all the hardness has been removed, a 'permanent lather' is formed, that is bubbles which last for at least one minute. The amount of soap added is a measure of the hardness.

Summary

1 The Earth is about 4500 million years old.

2 Rocks are usually classed as igneous, sedimentary or metamorphic.

3 Landscapes are formed by earth movements (which are very slow), weathering, erosion and deposition.

4 Earthquakes and volcanoes indicate that the Earth's crust is still moving.

5 Limestone is one of the naturally occurring forms of calcium carbonate.

6 Limestone is used for:
>   making concrete and cement.
>   building.
>   making iron from iron ore.
>   glass making.
> Slaked lime is used to neutralize acidity in the soil.

7 Calcium salts cause hardness in water which gives rise to 'fur' in pipes and wastes soap.

Questions

1 a What does the core of the Earth consist of?
  b What name is given to the layer between the core and the crust of the Earth?

2 In 1823 an American scientist Captain John Symmes announced his theory of the construction of the Earth. He said that it was made up of hollow balls, one inside the other. People lived on each ball and there were openings at the North and South poles to let them out. Suppose you were able to travel back in time and meet Captain Symmes. What would you say to him about his theory?

3 If the age of the Earth were all condensed into a single year, the human race would appear at ten minutes to midnight on 31 December! Use your library to find out the dates of some other important events in geological time, for example:
>   The ice ages.
>   First life appears.
>   Mammals appear.
> Work these out in terms of the Earth's 'year'.
> Present your findings in the most interesting way you can.

4 Use Fig 9.3 to explain:
 a Why Iceland is volcanic.
 b Why San Francisco has earthquakes.
 c Why Armenia had an earthquake in 1988.
 d Why the Himalayas are rising.

5 Fig 9.5 summarises what some scientists call the 'hydrological' cycle. Describe in your own words what happens in the cycle.

6 Explain the difference between:
 a An igneous and a sedimentary rock.
 b Limestone and sandstone.

7 Calcium carbonate is used in many ways in building. Write down as many of them as you can.

8 The table shows the ideal soil pH for growing these crops:
 wheat pH 6
 mint pH 8
 sugar beet pH 7
 a Which crop grows best in acidic soil?
 b Which crop grows best in alkaline soil?
 c A farmer wanted to grow sugar beet. The farm's soil was tested and found to have a pH of 5.
  (i) Suggest a substance that the farmer should add to the soil to make it more suitable for sugar beet.
  (ii) How does this substance change the pH of the soil?

9 When limestone is heated it forms quicklime (see Table 9.1).
 a How would the mass of quicklime compare with the mass of limestone?
 b Is the slaking of quicklime with water a mixing process or a chemical reaction? Give reasons for your answer.
 c How would you try to reconvert slaked lime into quicklime?
 d How would you try to reconvert quicklime into calcium carbonate?

10 Read the following passage carefully.
 Metal A reacts readily with water to give a colourless gas B and a milky sludge. Filtration of the sludge gives a white solid and a colourless solution C.
 The gas B can be trapped in an upside down test-tube and burns in air, forming a small amount of a colourless liquid D.
 The solution C goes milky when carbon dioxide is bubbled through it.
 a Use the above information to suggest a possible name for each substance A to D.
 b Explain the reasons for your answers.
 c How would you show that A is a metal (without destroying it)?
 d What would you expect the pH of solution C to be? Give a reason for your answer.

11 Magnesium carbonate (magnesite) decomposes more easily into a gas and another solid than calcium carbonate (calcite, limestone) does.

   a What gas and white solid would you get from magnesite?

   b The solid is less soluble than calcium oxide and forms a suspension in water that looks like 'milk of lime'. What name do you think is given to this suspension?

   c What medical use does this suspension have?

   d How would you expect magnesite to react with acids?

12 A data book gives the uses of limestone as:

cement manufacture	30 %
lime manufacture and agriculture	20 %
building stone and road ballast	20 %
blast furnace	15 %
glass making	10 %

   a Illustrate these on a bar chart.

   b Explain what is meant by 'lime manufacture and agriculture'.

   c Choose one of these uses and describe it in more detail, with diagrams.

13 Your parents are thinking of buying a water softener so that all your domestic water will be soft.

Would you recommend that they buy one? Give reasons for both sides of the argument.

Explorations 2

Always discuss your plans with your teacher before starting any practical work

I Explore the use of red cabbage as an indicator. (Cooked red cabbage will provide a suitable solution for your investigation.) At what pH values do colour changes occur? Find out if the same red colours are obtained from beetroot, blackberries, and blackcurrants and whether they would also make good indicators.

J Two companies advertise pills which they say relieve stomach ache by neutralizing the acid in the stomach.

Explore ways of comparing the pills chemically. (Do not try them on yourself or others!).

K You are provided with a supply of 'gripe water' which can be used as a medicine for curing stomach acidity. You are also provided with a bottle of malt vinegar and a bottle of wine vinegar.

Explore ways of finding out whether the two vinegars contain different concentrations of acid. How accurate can you be?

L You are provided with a sample of water which has both temporary and permanent hardness. Explore ways of finding out more about it. How accurately does your method let you measure the *amounts* of hardness?

M You are provided with several different salts, some of which cause hardness in water. Get together with your friends to explore ways of finding which salts cause hardness. Try to estimate how much hardness each causes.

Pool your results at the end. Present the group's results individually.

Chapter 10 Competition and the affinity series

10.1 Reactivity

In Chapter 8 we saw that it was convenient to divide metals into two classes – 'reactive' and 'everyday' metals. The reason that we meet everyday metals in our daily lives is that they are not very reactive and so do not react quickly with the water vapour or oxygen in the air. But within these two sets there is considerable variation. Gold will not tarnish in air while iron (in the same set) rusts slowly but surely. Therefore we could arrange all the metals in a 'reactivity series' with the 'reactive' metals, such as sodium, at the top, iron somewhere in the middle and gold near the bottom.

There is, however, a snag which we have to overcome when getting information to place the metals in the series. Iron can exist as a fine powder (iron filings) and as large chunks (for example, iron nails). The filings burn like the sparkler firework in Fig 10.1 overleaf, but the nail merely glows when heated. So reactivity depends not only on the nature of the metal, but also on its physical state (whether it is in very small or large pieces). A better way of arranging the metals in order is to let them compete with one another for a nonmetallic element, usually oxygen.

10.2 Affinity for oxygen

If magnesium powder and copper oxide are mixed together on an unreactive metal dish and the dish is then heated, a violent reaction occurs. This is much more violent than when magnesium powder on its own is heated in the same way. We therefore suspect that a reaction has taken place and we can represent the reaction by a 'word equation':

magnesium + copper oxide $\longrightarrow$ magnesium oxide + copper

The magnesium has 'grabbed' the oxygen from the copper oxide and we say that the magnesium has a greater **affinity** for the oxygen than copper.

Fig 10.1 A person with a sparkler.

Experiment 10.1
Affinity for oxygen

1 Mix a spatula of iron filings with a spatula of magnesium oxide in a crucible.

2 Heat the mixture over a Bunsen flame for a few minutes.

3 Examine the contents of the crucible. Black specks of iron and white specks of magnesium oxide can still be seen and there has been no reaction.

4 Mix a spatula of iron filings with a spatula of copper oxide in a crucible.

5 Heat this mixture over a Bunsen flame and watch what happens.

First a glow spreads through the mixture and then brown copper can be seen.
The word equation is:

copper oxide   +   iron $\longrightarrow$ copper   +   iron oxide

So we can say that iron has a greater affinity for oxygen than has copper, but a lesser affinity for oxygen than has magnesium.

We now have the beginning of an **affinity series**, which we can build up by doing more experiments. In each of these a metal must be heated with the oxide of another metal, so that the two metals will compete for the oxygen. **Some of these reactions are very violent, and you must only heat mixtures which your teacher recommends**. The two powders must be thoroughly mixed, otherwise the oxygen cannot easily be transferred from one metal to the other. The evidence for reaction will usually be a red glow; also the products will usually differ in appearance from the reactants.

Some metals have very similar affinities for oxygen and experiments such as these cannot distinguish between them. The table (Table 10.1) shows the relative affinities of some metals for oxygen.

Table 10.1 A simple affinity series of metals for oxygen.

sodium, magnesium, aluminium	greatest affinity
zinc	↑
iron	
copper, lead	
silver, gold	least affinity

Safety note

This experiment should only be done by a teacher. Eye protection and a safety screen are necessary.

10.3 Oxidation and reduction

As we saw in Chapter 4, the addition of oxygen is called **oxidation**. The removal of oxygen is called **reduction**. As an example, take the spectacular **thermit reaction**:

$$\text{aluminium} + \text{iron oxide} \longrightarrow \text{aluminium oxide} + \text{iron}$$

(Do **not** try this reaction yourself, your teacher may demonstrate it to you or show it on a video.)

The aluminium is *oxidized* to aluminium oxide and the iron oxide is *reduced* to iron. The iron oxide is the **oxidizing agent** (oxidant) since it supplies the oxygen which combines with the aluminium; the aluminium is the **reducing agent** (reductant) since it takes the oxygen away from the iron oxide.

The thermit reaction can be used to join (weld) two railway lines together. The iron oxide and aluminium mixture is poured into the gap and then ignited. The heat of the reaction partly melts the ends of the existing rails and a strong joint is made with the iron produced by the reaction (see Fig 10.2 overleaf).

Metals can reduce the oxides of metals which are below them in the affinity series, and metal oxides can be reduced by metals which are above them in the affinity series.

Fig 10.2

(a) Using the thermit reaction.

(b) the finished thermit weld.

10.4 The position of carbon

If carbon is heated with copper oxide in a test-tube, a glow is seen in the mixture and brown copper is present at the end:

carbon + copper oxide $\longrightarrow$ carbon dioxide + copper

The carbon has reduced the copper oxide to copper; if carbon is heated with magnesium oxide, no reaction occurs. Carbon must therefore be between magnesium and copper in the affinity series. Other experiments lead to carbon usually being placed just above iron in the series.

The word 'usually' in the last sentence is used because the position of carbon in the series depends on the temperature; above 800 °C carbon is higher than iron and thus should reduce iron oxide. A good Bunsen burner will just about reach this temperature. In industry, where temperatures well over 1000 °C can be reached, carbon can also reduce zinc oxide to zinc, a reaction which will not happen at the lower temperatures obtained with a Bunsen burner. There are two reasons why carbon is an important element for extracting metals from their ores: first it is cheap; second, the reaction produces carbon dioxide which is a gas and therefore easily got rid of, leaving just the solid metal (see also Section 11.2).

Metals above carbon in the series should reduce carbon dioxide. If a piece of burning magnesium is plunged into a gas jar

of carbon dioxide it continues to glow, and white and black specks appear on the sides of the gas jar:

magnesium + carbon dioxide ⟶ magnesium oxide + carbon
whiteblack

10.5 The reaction of metals with water and steam

Some of the most reactive metals will react with cold water. For example:

potassium moves around on a water surface, fizzes and catches fire. The water becomes alkaline;

sodium moves around on a water surface and fizzes, but it does not catch fire unless its movement is restricted. The water becomes alkaline;

calcium sinks, as it is denser than water, and starts reacting slowly, then more vigorously. A white cloudiness develops in the water and it becomes alkaline.

In each of these the reaction is the same:

metal + water ⟶ metal hydroxide + hydrogen

Sodium and potassium hydroxides are soluble and their presence can be detected by the alkalinity of the solution. Calcium hydroxide is less soluble and forms the white cloudiness. It is dangerous to try to collect the hydrogen in the reactions of sodium and potassium, but the reaction between calcium and water can be done in a beaker and the presence of hydrogen can easily be shown.

The test for hydrogen is that it explodes with a 'squeaky pop' when it is lit in the presence of oxygen. The gas can be collected in a test-tube of water placed over the calcium in the beaker (Fig 10.3). When the tube is full of gas, remove it from the water and very quickly place a lighted splint at its mouth. The 'pop' should be heard, but only if you have been quick enough – the hydrogen escapes rapidly.

These experiments show that the three metals are above hydrogen in the affinity series, since they reduce its oxide (remove the oxygen from water). It can also be seen that the metals have an *order* of reactivity: potassium (most reactive) then sodium, then calcium. These three elements are at the top of the affinity series.

The next metal in the affinity series, magnesium, will only react very slowly with water, even if it is heated. But it will react readily with steam (Fig 10.4a overleaf).

The reaction of magnesium is rather too fast for the hydrogen to be collected, but it can be lit at the end of the exit tube. Zinc and iron (being lower in the affinity series) react more slowly with steam, and the hydrogen can be collected over water (Fig 10.4b).

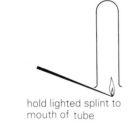

hold lighted splint to
mouth of tube

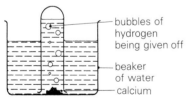

bubbles of
hydrogen
being given off

beaker
of water

calcium

Fig 10.3 Testing for hydrogen.

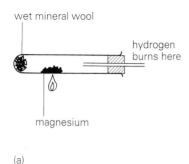

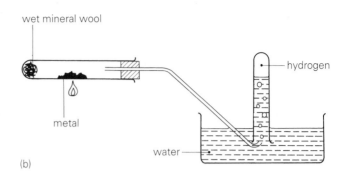

(a)

(b)

Fig 10.4 The action of steam on metals.

In each case the reaction is:

metal   +   steam   ⟶   metal oxide   +   hydrogen

hydrogen oxide

The oxides of the metals can be seen in the test-tubes.

Metals below iron in the affinity series will not react with steam, so we can say that hydrogen comes just below iron in the affinity series. The affinity series is given in Appendix 3.

10.6 Reduction of metal oxides with hydrogen

Fig 10.5 The action of hydrogen on metal oxides.

Since hydrogen is above copper and lead in the affinity series it can be used to reduce their oxides. The apparatus of Fig 10.5a can be used.

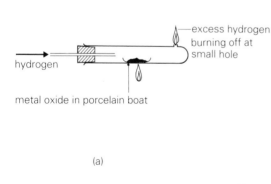

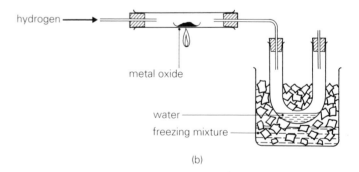

(a)

(b)

 **Safety note**

This experiment must only be done by a teacher. Safety screens must be used.

Hydrogen (from a cylinder) is passed over the heated metal oxide and the excess is burned off at the small hole. The oxide should not be heated until the hydrogen has been ignited. The gas must **never** be ignited at the hole until it is certain that all the air has been pushed out of the tube, otherwise an explosion will occur there. To ensure that all the air has been pushed out, tubes of hydrogen should be collected and tested (with a Bunsen burner at least a metre away from the experiment) until they burn steadily. The jet must then be lit *only* from the hydrogen burning in the test-tube. Black copper oxide turns to brown copper which will conduct electricity. Yellow lead oxide

Safety note

Hydrogen explodes when mixed with air and ignited. This symbol marks explosive chemicals.

turns grey, and shiny globules of molten lead are seen. The equation for both reactions is:

$$metal\ oxide\ +\ hydrogen\ \longrightarrow\ metal\ +\ \underset{hydrogen\ oxide}{steam}$$

If the apparatus shown in Fig 10.5b is used, water can be condensed and tested as in Section 3.6.

Fig 10.6 Displacement reactions: copper coated steel knife in copper sulphate solution, silver crystals on copper wire in silver nitrate solution, lead crystals on zinc in lead nitrate solution.

10.7 The displacement series

If an iron penknife blade is dipped in copper sulphate solution it becomes coated with copper. The iron is said to have **displaced** (pushed out) the copper from the copper sulphate. The word equation is:

$$iron\ +\ \underset{solution}{\underset{sulphate}{copper}}\ \longrightarrow\ \underset{solution}{\underset{sulphate}{iron}}\ +\ copper$$

Experiment 10.2
Displacement reactions

1 Put a spatula measure of iron powder in a test-tube.

2 Add about half a test-tube of copper sulphate solution.

3 Cork the tube and shake it vigorously. Let the liquid settle.

4 Look closely at the contents of the test-tube.

5 Try other metals and look for evidence of a reaction.

The black iron powder was replaced by brown copper and the blue copper sulphate solution was replaced by a pale green (almost colourless) iron sulphate solution. This reaction takes place with any soluble copper salt.

Other displacement reactions include:

$$copper\ +\ \underset{solution}{silver\ nitrate}\ \longrightarrow\ \underset{solution}{copper\ nitrate}\ +\ silver$$

If a copper wire is placed in silver nitrate solution, the solution turns blue because of the copper nitrate that is formed and grey needle-shaped crystals of silver are formed on the copper.

$$zinc\ +\ \underset{solution}{lead\ nitrate}\ \longrightarrow\ \underset{solution}{zinc\ nitrate}\ +\ lead$$

When a piece of zinc is placed in lead nitrate solution, crystals of lead begin to grow on it; this is excellent evidence for a reaction, even though the solution does not change colour, since both the nitrates are colourless (Fig 10.6).

Table 10.2 A displacement series for metals.

magnesium	most reactive
zinc	↑
iron	
nickel, tin	
lead	
copper	
silver	least reactive

By placing metals in solutions of salts of other metals and seeing whether reactions occur it is possible to build up a **displacement series** (Table 10.2). Metals at the top will react with the solutions of salts of metals lower down, and the lower metal is displaced.

The displacement series is very similar to – but not exactly the same as – the affinity series. It can be used to separate some metals where experiments using oxides do not give satisfactory results (for example lead and copper). However, in some displacement experiments it is not easy to decide whether there is positive evidence of a reaction. For example, it is difficult to decide which is the higher of nickel and tin. In these cases the electrochemical series can be of use (see Additional material at the end of Chapter 13).

Safety note

Sulphur dioxide is toxic.

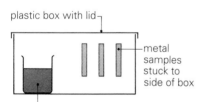

plastic box with lid

metal samples stuck to side of box

beaker containing sodium metabisulphite. This fills the box with damp sulphur dioxide

Fig 10.7.

Safety note

Dilute acids are harmful.

Safety note

Hydrogen is explosive.

10.8 The effect of acids on metals

Sulphur dioxide and nitrogen dioxide, are present in polluted air (see page 45) and in acid rain (see page 79) since they are acid gases. Metals which are exposed to these gases are found to corrode (Fig 10.7). This corrosion can be minimised by painting the metal or by covering it in grease.

When some metals are added to solutions of acids, hydrogen is produced. The gas can be collected and tested as in Section 10.5. For example:

zinc + hydrogen sulphate ⟶ hydrogen + zinc sulphate
sulphuric acid

As in Section 6.3 we have written 'hydrogen sulphate' for sulphuric acid. This reaction is another example of displacement; zinc is displacing hydrogen from the acid. On the other hand, metals like copper and lead do not react with acids. These experiments show us that hydrogen is between iron and lead in the displacement series. They also add something to our understanding of the word 'acid'. We can now define an acid as a substance containing hydrogen which can be displaced by a reactive metal.

The general reaction between acids and the metals above hydrogen in the displacement series can be written:

metal + acid ⟶ hydrogen + salt

for example:

magnesium + hydrogen chloride ⟶ hydrogen + magnesium chlo
hydrochloric acid

iron + hydrogen sulphate ⟶ hydrogen + iron sulphate
sulphuric acid

Nitric acid has some unusual properties and does not always react in the same way as the other acids.

Summary

1 Metals can be arranged in order of their affinity for oxygen in an **affinity series**. If a metal is heated with the oxide of a metal *below* it in the series, a reaction occurs, for example:

magnesium + copper oxide ⟶ magnesium oxide + copper

2 Oxidation is the addition of oxygen.
Reduction is the removal of oxygen.
Oxidizing agents (oxidants) oxidize other substances.
Reducing agents (reductants) reduce other substances.

3 The nonmetal carbon has a place in the affinity series which varies with temperature. Carbon is useful as an industrial reducing agent.

4 Metals high in the affinity series react with water like this:

metal + water ⟶ metal hydroxide + hydrogen

Metals lower in the affinity series (but still above hydrogen) react with *steam*:

metal + steam ⟶ metal oxide + hydrogen

5 Hydrogen will reduce the oxides of metals which are below it in the affinity series:

metal oxide + hydrogen ⟶ metal + steam

6 The **displacement series** is very similar to the affinity series. A metal high in the series will displace a metal *below* it from a solution of the lower metal's salt, for example:

copper + silver nitrate ⟶ silver + copper nitrate

7 Metals above hydrogen in the affinity series react with hydrochloric acid and sulphuric acid like this:

metal + acid ⟶ hydrogen + salt

Thus some metals corrode in air which is polluted by acids.

Questions

1 Nickel does not react with zinc oxide.
Nickel reacts with lead oxide to form lead and nickel oxide.
  a Place the elements lead, nickel and zinc in order of their affinity for oxygen. (Most *reactive* first.)
  What, if anything, would you expect to happen if you
  b heated a mixture of zinc and lead oxide?
  c heated a mixture of lead and zinc oxide?

2 When black copper oxide reacts with black carbon in a test-tube a shiny red-brown solid can be clearly seen once the tube has cooled.
  a What is the red-brown solid?
  b Write a word equation for this reaction.
  c How would you test for the gas that is formed?
  d When this reaction takes place on a crucible lid, very little of the red-brown solid can be seen at the end. Why is this?
  e What is meant by oxidation and reduction?
  f In this reaction which substance is oxidized and which is reduced?
  g Does carbon or copper have the greater affinity for oxygen?

3 Imagine that the bottles of copper oxide and powdered carbon in a laboratory have lost their labels. They are both black powders. It is necessary to find out which of the bottles contains which substance.
  Describe in detail two experiments by which you could make quite sure which bottle contains which substance.

4 You are provided with a sample of an element X. Describe suitable experiments:
  a To find out whether it is a metal:
   (i) Using physical properties.
   (ii) Using chemical properties.
  b To find its position in the affinity series.

5 When a piece of burning calcium is lowered into a gas jar of carbon dioxide, two solids, one white and one black, are formed.
  a What is the black solid?
  b What is the white solid?
  c The white solid is slightly soluble in water. What is the solution called?
  d Use this reaction to explain what is meant by oxidation and reduction.
  e Has carbon or calcium the greater affinity for oxygen?

6 Zinc reacts with iron oxide when they are heated together.
  a Write the word equation for the reaction.
  b Explain what you mean by 'reduction' by reference to the equation.
  c Give two reasons why zinc is not used in industry to make iron from its ore.

7 a Why is carbon (coke) used to extract iron from iron ore (iron oxide)?
  b What else will be produced?
  c Why is carbon not used to extract aluminium from aluminium oxide?

8 Substances X, Y and Z are gold, magnesium and copper oxide (not necessarily in that order).
Solid X – did not react when heated in steam, but when it was heated in hydrogen, water was formed and the solid lost mass.
Solid Y – did not react with either steam or hydrogen even on strong heating.
Solid Z – did not react when heated in hydrogen, but when heated in steam, hydrogen was formed and the solid gained mass.

a Why is solid X not a metallic element?
b Why is solid Y not magnesium?
c Explain how it is possible for a substance to gain in mass when heated in steam.
d Why is solid Z not gold?
e Identify the solids X, Y and Z.

9 The following is an affinity (activity) series, written in order of decreasing reactivity:
magnesium, carbon, iron, hydrogen, copper.
In each of the following cases state what products, if any, you would expect to obtain on heating these pairs of substances together.

a Magnesium + carbon dioxide.
b Iron + steam.
c Copper + iron oxide.

10 Liquid sodium is used as a coolant in some nuclear power stations. Rigorous precautions are taken to ensure that no water gets to the sodium. Why is this?

11 a When hydrogen burns with a pop, what is formed?
b Why does impure hydrogen often burn with a loud pop, while pure hydrogen often burns without making a noise?
c When hydrogen is prepared in a large apparatus it must always be collected *before* it is tested. Why is it dangerous to try to light the hydrogen as it comes out of the apparatus?

12 When hydrogen is passed over gently heated aluminium oxide, nothing is observed to happen. When hydrogen is passed over gently heated copper oxide, a red glow spreads through the solid, drops of condensed moisture are seen and then a reddish powder is left which conducts electricity.

a What do you conclude about hydrogen being more or less active than aluminium or copper?
b Account for the observations made in the case of the copper oxide.

13 a Explain why an iron nail becomes pink-brown if placed in copper sulphate solution.
b Explain why a piece of copper becomes pale grey when placed in silver nitrate solution. (The solution turns from colourless to blue.)

c Place the metals copper, iron and silver in order of increasing reactivity.

d What would you expect to happen if a piece of silver were dropped into iron sulphate solution?

14 I made up a solution of copper sulphate to kill the blackspot on my roses. I noticed the iron watering can I had used had turned brown inside. Why was this? (Give a word equation).

15 The apparatus shown in Fig 10.8 is used for making and collecting hydrogen.

a Copy the diagram, completing it so that it will work effectively.

b Name one pair of substances, X and Y, which might be used in the apparatus.

c The first test-tube of gas collected from the above apparatus may be somewhat different from the rest. Why is this so?

d What test would you use to show that the gas was hydrogen?

e Why is hydrogen sometimes used in balloons?

f Why may this be dangerous?

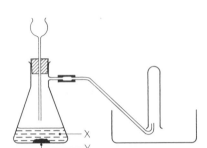

Fig 10.8.

16 A council waste incinerator will produce fumes of hydrochloric acid if the plastic PVC is burnt in it. The council have arranged to absorb these fumes and claim success because a copper roof nearby has not turned rapidly green (the colour of copper chloride).

a How would you explain to the Chief Executive of the council that this does not prove anything?

b Would it make a difference if the roof were made of corrugated iron?

17 In an experiment to investigate the reaction of magnesium in dilute hydrochloric acid, a chemist took several 2-cm lengths of magnesium ribbon and placed them in equal volumes of acid of different concentrations. The time taken for the magnesium to disappear was measured and the results shown in Fig 10.9 were obtained.

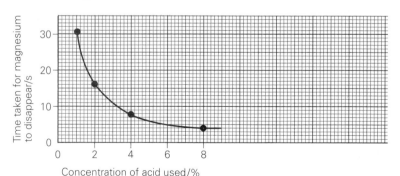

Fig 10.9.

a How long would it take for 2-cm of ribbon to disappear in 3 % acid?

b If the concentration of acid is doubled, what is the effect on the time taken for the magnesium to disappear?

c When the chemist used acid of less than 1 % concentration the reaction became very slow and eventually stopped, leaving some of the magnesium. Explain why the reaction stopped.

d The chemist also recorded that a piece of ribbon that had been stored for a long time did not fizz much for the first few seconds after it was put into the acid. Why do you think this was so?

e Suggest one factor the chemist might vary in further investigation of this reaction.

18 (Difficult) The apparatus shown in Fig 10.10 can be used to investigate the action of carbon dioxide on heated metals. The sodium hydroxide solution absorbs any excess carbon dioxide.

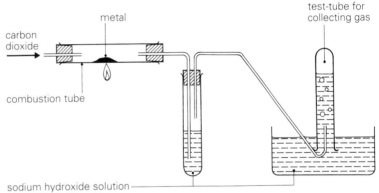

Fig 10.10.

The experiment was first performed using magnesium.

a Write a word equation for the reaction which occurs.

b Describe what you would *see* in the combustion tube when the magnesium reacted.

c State with reasons whether you would expect any gas to be collected in the test-tube.

The experiment was repeated using zinc. A yellow residue (white when cool) was formed in the combustion tube and a gas collected in the test-tube. This gas burned with a blue flame and was not a zinc compound.

d Say with reasons what the gas must be.

e How could you test the gas to prove your conclusion in **d**?

f Write a word equation for the reaction.

Sample	Mass of black solid	Mass of residue
A	3.6 g	2.4 g
B	6.4 g	5.1 g
C	4.3 g	3.4 g
D	4.7 g	4.3 g
E	7.6 g	5.2 g
F	8.9 g	7.1 g

19 (Difficult) Some students heated samples from bottles labelled 'black copper oxide' in a stream of hydrogen until no further change occurred. They weighed the black solid before heating and the residue which remained after heating.
   Their results are in the table on the left.
The samples came from three different bottles and it was suggested that some of the bottles contained impurities. Pure copper oxide contains 80 % by mass of copper.
   a Plot a graph of *mass of residue* against *mass of black solid* (horizontal axis).
   b Use the graph to identify which samples came from which of the three different bottles.
   c Did any of the bottles contain pure copper oxide? Explain your reasoning.
   d Suggest the kinds of impurities which might have been present in the other bottles.

20 (Difficult) When dilute nitric acid is added to copper (in a fume cupboard) a brown acidic gas is given off and the solution turns blue.
   a The gas is an oxide. Which oxide is it? (Refer back to Chapter 4 if you need help.)
   b Which element might be in the blue solution? (Think of other blue solutions.)
   c What do you think the blue solution might be?
   d Would hydrogen be given off as well as the brown gas?

21 (Difficult) Here are the results of five experiments A–E in which magnesium is added to hydrochloric acid and hydrogen is produced. The total volume of hydrogen is shown and the time taken for it to be produced.

	Magnesium	Acid	Hydrogen	Time
A	0.2 g of powder	50 cm^3 of 4 M	200 cm^3	½ min
B	0.2 g of ribbon	50 cm^3 of 4 M	200 cm^3	2 min
C	0.2 g of powder	60 cm^3 of 4 M	200 cm^3	½ min
D	0.2 g of powder	10 cm^3 of 4 M	48 cm^3	¼ min
E	0.2 g of ribbon	100 cm^3 of 2 M	200 cm^3	4 min
F	0.2 g of ribbon	100 cm^3 of 4 M		
G	0.2 g of powder	200 cm^3 of M		

Note: M is a measure of the acid concentration. Thus a 4 M solution is twice as concentrated as a 2 M solution, in other words it contains twice as much acid in the same volume.

   a How are the results affected when magnesium ribbon is used instead of powder?
   b Explain why the results of experiments A and C are the same.
   c Why are the results of experiments A and D different?
   d Predict the results which would be obtained in experiments F and G. Give your reasons.

Chapter 11   Metals from minerals

11.1 Rocks, minerals and ores

As we saw in Chapter 9, minerals are concentrations of useful chemicals found in rocks; they may be elements or, more often, compounds. We have already met limestone (Section 9.4) which is in itself a useful material. It is also the source of a wide range of lime products (Section 9.5). Minerals from which metals can be obtained are called ores. To obtain metals from minerals, three stages are necessary. First the ore has to be concentrated, for many ores are found embedded in useless rock. Then the metal has to be extracted chemically from the ore. Finally, the metal may have to be purified or made into an alloy.

Not all the elements are equally common on Earth. Excluding the core (inside) of the Earth, the approximate percentages (of the total mass) of the different elements are shown in Fig 11.1.

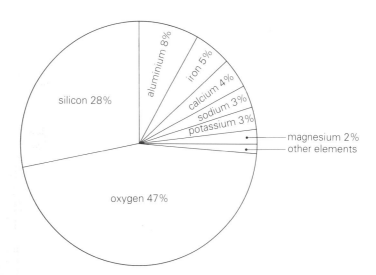

Fig 11.1 The composition of the Earth's crust.

None of the other common everyday metals (copper, lead, tin, zinc) come in the top twenty and none are as common as 0.01 %. You will notice that silicon and oxygen are by far the most common; rocks contain a great deal of silicon oxide (sand and quartz) as well as compounds known as silicates (which contain both silicon and oxygen) and alumino-silicates (containing aluminium, silicon and oxygen). These compounds have to be separated and removed from the more valuable mineral. This separation usually uses physical differences. For example, the ore can be crushed and the mineral separated from the useless rock using the fact that the rock and the mineral have very different densities.

11.2 Extraction of the metal

When the mineral has been concentrated, the problem now is to extract the metal. The method used depends on the position of the metal in the affinity series (Chapter 10 and Appendix 3). Metals that are very low in the series sometimes occur native: that is, as the pure metal. One such example is gold. Another unreactive metal is mercury which sometimes occurs native, but more often as compounds which decompose easily when they are heated, giving the metal.

The more reactive everyday metals (those between zinc and copper in the affinity series) have to be prepared by chemical reduction. The ore is often an oxide or else can easily be converted into an oxide. It is then a question of finding a reducing agent that can remove the oxygen from the oxide. The one that is used most often is carbon (coke, made by heating coal). It has the great advantage of being cheap, for coal can easily be dug out of the ground. In addition the oxide of carbon is a gas, which means that there is no problem about separating the metal and the carbon oxide, the products of the reaction. Coke is also strong and mixes well with the oxide that is to be reduced. In contrast, compare carbon with another possible reducing agent, aluminium. This is very expensive, for it has to be extracted by electrolysis: also, its oxide is a solid, which makes separation of the products difficult.

The very reactive metals (such as aluminium, magnesium and sodium) have to be prepared using electrolysis (Chapter 13).

11.3 Purification and alloy making

Having extracted our metal, we are faced with the problem of purification. The degree of purification will depend on what the metal is to be used for. It may involve further reduction, or electrolysis.

Alloys are mixtures or compounds of metals with other elements. Steels are alloys of iron and carbon. They are harder than iron if they contain the right amount of carbon. Steels that are used for special jobs often have other metals added as well; for example, stainless steel also contains chromium and nickel. Other alloys include brass (copper and zinc), bronze (copper and tin) and amalgams (mercury with other metals).

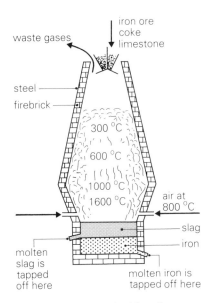

Fig 11.2 Diagram of a blast furnace.

11.4 Iron and steel

Iron is the most widely used metal, both by itself and in steels. It is quite common (Fig 11.1) and is made from its ores by reduction with carbon. The reaction is carried out in towers 60 metres high known as **blast furnaces**; these are also used in the purification of lead and zinc (Figs 11.2 and 11.3). At the top of the furnace, iron ore (iron oxide and rock), coke and limestone are fed in. At the bottom of the furnace hot air at 800 °C is blasted in (hence the name) and this reacts with some of the coke to raise the temperature higher still. At the bottom of the furnace the temperature is about 1600 °C, at which temperature the iron is a liquid. The overall reaction is:

iron oxide + carbon $\longrightarrow$ carbon dioxide + iron

The rock in the ore would still be solid at this temperature and it would rapidly block up the furnace. The limestone is added to convert the rock to a liquid mixture called slag. One of the main

Fig 11.3 Blast furnace.

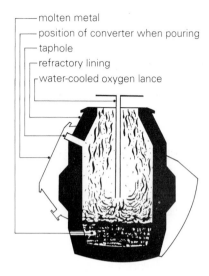

— molten metal
— position of converter when pouring
— taphole
— refractory lining
— water-cooled oxygen lance

Fig 11.4 The basic oxygen furnace.

Table 11.1 Uses of three types of steel.

substances in slag is calcium silicate which is formed from the silicon oxide in the rock:

$$\text{calcium carbonate} \xrightarrow{\text{heat}} \text{calcium oxide} + \text{carbon dioxide}$$
limestone

$$\underset{\text{solid}}{\text{calcium oxide}} + \underset{\text{solid}}{\text{silicon oxide}} \longrightarrow \underset{\text{liquid}}{\text{calcium silicate}}$$

The slag (being less dense) floats on the iron. The liquid slag and the impure liquid iron (known as pig iron) are both run out of the furnace at intervals and then solidify. The slag can be used in road-making, though, too often in the past, it was piled up into heaps which spoiled the appearance of the landscape.

The impure pig iron contains 3–4 % carbon from the coke and is very brittle. Much of this iron is turned into steel and this involves removing most of the carbon but leaving enough to give steel its strength. Steel is made by a number of processes, all of which involve oxidizing the excess carbon by blowing oxygen or air over or through molten iron.

The method most widely used today is the **basic oxygen furnace** (Fig. 11.4). Pure oxygen is blown into the furnace using a water-cooled copper lance, a hollow tube. The carbon is oxidized to carbon dioxide which is blown out. Limestone is also added (limestone is the 'base') to remove impurities, such as silica, as slag. Different types of steel have different percentages of carbon as shown in Table 11.1. Special steels have other metals added to improve their properties; for example stainless steel contains chromium and nickel.

Type	Percentage carbon	Description	Some uses
mild steel	0.1–0.2	fairly soft and malleable	boiler plates, rivets, nuts and bolts
medium-carbon steel	0.2–0.7	less malleable and harder	rails, axles, castings
high-carbon steel	0.7–1.5	not very malleable, but very hard	hammers, machine tools, cutting tools

Background Reading

The cost of iron and steel making

A modern blast furnace can make 3000 tonnes of iron per day. In order to do this the following amounts of ore, coke and limestone are used in the furnace:

ore	5000 tonnes
coke	1500 tonnes
limestone	500 tonnes

The cost of these (in 1986) were:

ore £10 per tonne
coke £44 per tonne
limestone £3 per tonne

The resulting iron can be sold as cast iron plate at £42 per tonne. Steel can be sold for £106 per tonne. Slag fetches £1 per tonne and 1000 tonnes of slag are produced with 3000 tonnes of iron.

Questions

1 a Work out the daily cost of the ore, coke and limestone.
   b Which costs most?
   c Does this surprise you?

2 How much money per day can be made by selling:
   a the slag
   b the iron as cast iron plate?
   c overall?

3 What is the 'profit'?

4 What is this 'profit' used for? (Are there any costs not mentioned above?)

5 a Steel can be sold for a much higher price. What extra costs are involved in making it?
   b Would you expect the 'profit' on steel to be higher?

Siting the steel industry

The map (Fig 11.5 overleaf) shows the position of coalfields and limestone and iron ore deposits in this country. At the end of the nineteenth century, iron was being produced at sites near both coal and iron ore deposits. However, the iron ore mined in this country is low grade (it contains a low proportion of iron). Modern developments in the steel industry require large quantities of high grade ore. Much of this is imported from overseas, especially South America, Canada and Africa. It is economical to do this because enormous ships can carry over 30 000 tons of ore at a time.

Coke is made from coal, some of which is imported in spite of the large number of active coal mines in this country. Limestone comes from mines in this country.

Blast furnaces are ugly and they tend to produce air pollution:
a sulphur dioxide – an acid gas.
b smoke, grit, dust and fine particles of iron oxide.

Modern plants make every effort to minimize these pollutants. Large amounts of water for cooling purposes are also needed and the water is sometimes slightly contaminated.

Questions

1 a Look at the map (Fig 11.5) and pick a place well inland where iron and steel probably used to be produced before imported ore was used.
   b Why did you choose as you did?

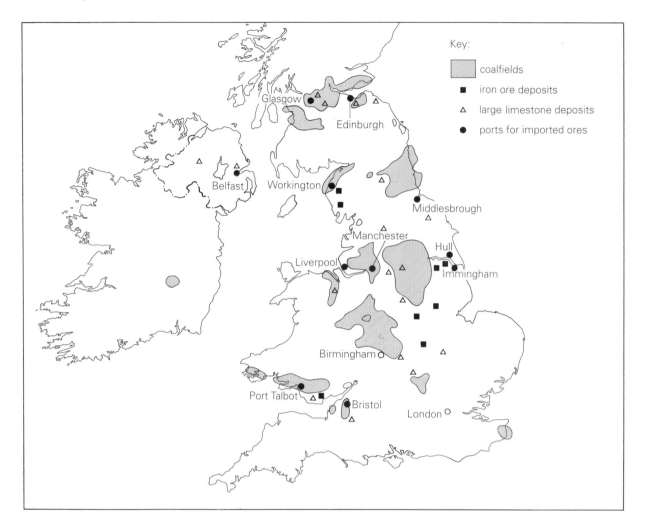

Fig 11.5.

2 What effect will modern changes in the iron and steel industry have had on the people in the place you mentioned in your answer to question **1**?

3 a If you were General Manager of British Steel describe one site where you would build a modern iron and steel works.
b Explain your choice.

4 The main plants of British Steel are concentrated in South Wales, Teeside, Humberside and Clydeside. Use an atlas (if necessary) to see if your choice in **3** is in one of these areas.

5 Imagine you were the chairperson of the residents association in the area you mentioned in **3**. Write a speech to a local meeting outlining your reasons against the building of a blast furnace in your area.

6 Write a speech that a representative of British Steel might make to argue against the speech in **5**.

11.5 Corrosion and its prevention
(See also Section 7.4.)

Although we can get metals from ores, the reverse process is the one that occurs naturally and we are always having to fight to prevent metals corroding. The higher a metal comes in the affinity series, the greater the corrosion problem can be. Indoors copper does not corrode and out-of-doors it is many years before a copper roof reacts with the gases in the atmosphere to give the beautiful green colour of the compounds that form on the surface of the copper. Iron, however, rusts much more rapidly and the following ways have been devised to prevent the rusting:

1 Make it into stainless steel. This is expensive.

2 Paint it. This prevents the iron from coming into contact with the oxygen and water in the atmosphere.

3 Coat it (plate it) with a layer of a less reactive metal (such as tin or chromium) to keep away the oxygen and water.

4 Cover it with a more reactive metal (for example, galvanize it with zinc) so that the more reactive metal corrodes rather than the iron.

Corrosion is a considerable problem costing thousands of millions of pounds a year. It is worth spending money to prevent it, especially as a lot of money has been spent obtaining the metal from the ore in the first place.

Summary

1 The stages in obtaining a metal from a mineral are:
   a Concentration of the ore.
   b Chemical extraction of the metal.
   c Purification or alloy making.

2 Metals low in the affinity series occur native. Everyday metals in the middle of the affinity series are extracted by carbon reduction of their oxides. Metals high in the affinity series are extracted by electrolysis of their molten salts.

3 Zinc, iron and lead are extracted from their ores by carbon reduction in a blast furnace.

4 Iron is made into steel by blowing oxygen through the molten mass until most of the carbon has been oxidized.

5 Corrosion (especially rusting) wastes money and it can be prevented.

Questions

1 a Which are the two most common elements in the Earth's crust?
b Which is the most common metal?
c What three stages have to be carried out to obtain a pure metal from an impure ore?

2 a Give as many reasons as you can why in industry carbon is a more useful reducing agent than magnesium.
b Could hydrogen be used as an industrial reducing agent? Consider its advantages and disadvantages compared with carbon and magnesium.

3 a In a blast furnace what is the reason for:
(i) The blast of hot air?
(ii) The coke?
(iii) The limestone?
b What liquid products come out of the furnace?
c Air is blasted in. What gases come out of the top of the furnace?

4 Suggest reasons why:
a Lead, rather than iron, is used on church roofs.
b Iron rusts very slowly in a desert, more quickly next to a freshwater lake and very rapidly near the sea.
c Copper, not the cheaper iron, is used for water pipes.
d Iron greenhouse frames are painted with aluminium paint.
e A steel car bumper rusts quickly if the chromium plating breaks.

5 Give one advantage and one disadvantage in each case for the following uses for metals:
a Silver for coins.
b Lead for water pipes.
c Iron for bridges.

6 In the thermit process (see page 113), aluminium powder is mixed with the oxide of either iron, chromium or certain other metals. On ignition by a fuse the oxide is reduced to the metal, which is molten at the temperature of the reaction. Welding of steel rails can be carried out by packing a mixture of aluminium powder and iron oxide round the joint and igniting the mixture with a fuse.
a What does this tell you about the relative positions of aluminium, iron and chromium in the affinity series?
b Name another metal which could be extracted from its oxide using the thermit process.
c Write a word equation for the reaction between aluminium and chromium oxide.
d Iron is not made commercially by the thermit process. Suggest a reason for this.
e Explain what happens when the thermit process is used to weld steel rails together.

7 a An ore of lead can be converted into lead oxide by heating but heat alone will not convert it into the metal. If you were given some of the lead oxide, how would you try to obtain some metallic lead from it? Describe the experiment and say how you would know whether it had been successful.

b When lead is melted in a crucible the shiny surface of the molten metal soon becomes tarnished. Suggest a reason for this, and suggest a way of melting lead without letting the surface become tarnished.

c It is not difficult to obtain metallic lead from its ore, so why is lead sufficiently valuable for it to be worthwhile for thieves to steal it?

8 Iron is made industrially in a blast furnace where iron ore (iron oxide) is reduced to iron by coke (carbon). Hot air is blown into the bottom of the furnace and waste gases leave at the top. Limestone is also added to the furnace. Impure iron and slag run out of the bottom of the furnace.

a What does reduction mean?

b Write a word equation for the reaction in the furnace.

c Name the waste gases leaving the furnace.

d (i) Can sodium reduce iron oxide?
(ii) Why isn't sodium used instead of carbon in the blast furnace?

e Why do you think carbon is chosen as the reductant (reducing agent) rather than a metal which is at about the same place in the affinity series as carbon?

f What do you think is the main impurity in the iron?

g Describe an experiment you could carry out to see if carbon will reduce iron oxide in the laboratory. What signs of reaction would you look for?

Chapter 12   Analysis of simple salts

12.1 What are salts?

We first met salts in Section 6.3 where we found that they were the product of neutralization reactions. Salts can be recognized from their names; the first part is usually the name of a metal, the second is usually a name based on a nonmetal. Thus copper sulphate, copper chloride and copper nitrate are all **copper salts**. The same 'nonmetal parts', sulphate, chloride and nitrate will go with sodium to make a series of sodium salts, and so on. The commonest 'nonmetal parts' are: bromide, carbonate, chloride, iodide, nitrate, phosphate, sulphide and sulphate. Remember those ending in *-ide* contain one nonmetal only; thus sodium sulph*ide* is a compound which contains just sodium and sulphur. Those ending in *-ate* contain the nonmetal and *oxygen*. Thus sodium sulph*ate* contains sodium, sulphur and oxygen.

Salts are found dissolved in the sea, in rocks and in evaporated deposits. One of the chemist's jobs is to find out the composition of substances, that is which elements they contain. The process is called **analysis** and this chapter is about some of the simpler ways in which salts can be analysed.

12.2 Some preliminary tests

Before testing for one or other metal or nonmetal, a chemist wants to be able to do some general tests to get some idea of what a substance might be. These tests are:

1 Appearance
The colour of a salt often tells us something about the metal part, for example:
copper salts are blue or green;
iron salts are green or brown.

2 The effect of heating in a dry test-tube
To the trained eye this test can reveal a lot about a substance. Some simple results are:
a Colour change,
for example: if lead is present the residue will be orange when hot and yellow when cold;
if zinc is present the residue will be yellow when hot and white when cold.

Safety note

Only heat very small amounts of unknown solids – you never know what will happen!

b A gas is evolved:
carbon dioxide from a *carbonate*;
water vapour from a *hydrated salt.*

3 Is it soluble in water?
To perform this test, shake very little of the solid with half a test-tube of water. Do not expect a great heap of powder to dissolve!
Here are some simple rules:
all *sodium* and *potassium* salts are soluble;
all *nitrates* are soluble;
all *chlorides* are soluble except lead chloride and silver chloride;
all *sulphates* are soluble except barium sulphate and lead sulphate;
all *carbonates* are *insoluble* except those of sodium and potassium.

4 Action of dilute acid
If dilute hydrochloric acid is added to certain salts, gases are evolved. The most usual is *carbon dioxide* from a *carbonate.*

Safety note

Only add acid to very
small quantities
of unknown solids.

12.3 Tests for the metal part

Some idea of the nature of the metal may have been obtained from preliminary tests, particularly if the metal has coloured salts. However, a **flame test** is always worth doing as it is a quick and easy way of distinguishing between many metals.

Experiment 12.1
Flame tests

Safety note

Concentrated hydrochloric
acid is corrosive—be careful.

Safety note

Solid calcium chloride and
solid barium chloride are
harmful.

Safety note

Solid copper chloride is
toxic.

1 Stick a piece of nichrome wire, 7–8 cm long into a cork to make a handle. (Nichrome is a nickel-chromium alloy which does not colour a flame on its own.)

2 Put a few drops of concentrated hydrochloric acid in a watch glass.

3 Dip the tip of the nichrome wire into the acid and then place it in the *side* of a roaring Bunsen flame (not the blue cone). The wire is clean when the flame is no longer coloured.

4 Dip the end of the clean wire into the acid again and then into the sample of chemical to be tested. A little will stick to the wire.

5 Put the wire into the Bunsen flame as before. If the flame is not coloured, it is better to put the wire into the acid again, rather into the solid, before returning it to the flame.

6 A flame colour can then often be seen and the metal part of the chemical can be identified from Table 12.1 (overleaf).

Table 12.1 Flame colours of some common metals.

potassium	lilac (pale mauve)
sodium	*intense* yellow (pale yellow is probably due to small sodium impurity)
calcium	red
barium	apple green
lead	blue
copper	blue-green (with white flashes)

The colour is given by *all* salts of the metal concerned. The concentrated acid converts them all to the chlorides which vaporize well in the flame.

The commonest metals which do not have a flame colour are magnesium, zinc and iron. Iron can often be recognized by the colour of its compounds (green or brown) and zinc by the colour of the residue after heating the salt (yellow when hot, white when cold). Magnesium has no coloured compounds and a special reagent is needed to help identify it, called magneson 1 solution. The suspected magnesium salt is dissolved in water and a few drops of magneson 1 are added, followed by an equal volume of dilute sodium hydroxide solution. If magnesium is present, a blue precipitate* will develop in the pink solution. This test should be carried out only if other metals have been shown to be absent since some of them might also give a similar precipitate.

Safety note

2 M dilute nitric acid is irritant.

Safety note

Barium chloride solution is harmful.

12.4 Tests for the nonmetal part

There is no general test for the nonmetal part similar to the flame test for metals, so we will restrict ourselves to identifying carbonate, sulphate and chloride.

Carbonate will already have been identified in the preliminary test with hydrochloric acid. If carbonate is not present, the salt should be dissolved in dilute nitric acid and divided into two parts.

a Test one part with silver nitrate solution. If a white precipitate of insoluble silver chloride is formed it indicates that the salt is a *chloride*.

b Test the other part with barium chloride solution. If a white precipitate of insoluble barium sulphate is formed it indicates that the salt is a *sulphate*.

There is no simple test for the other common nonmetal part which is *nitrate*.

12.5 Summary of methods of analysis

A flow diagram which summarizes the previous sections is given in Table 12.2. Much more complicated schemes are available to more advanced chemists, but at every level the best analytical chemists are the ones who keep their eyes (and their noses) open and think about what they observe, rather than just plodding through the scheme.

* A precipitate is a solid substance which is formed when two clear solutions are mixed.

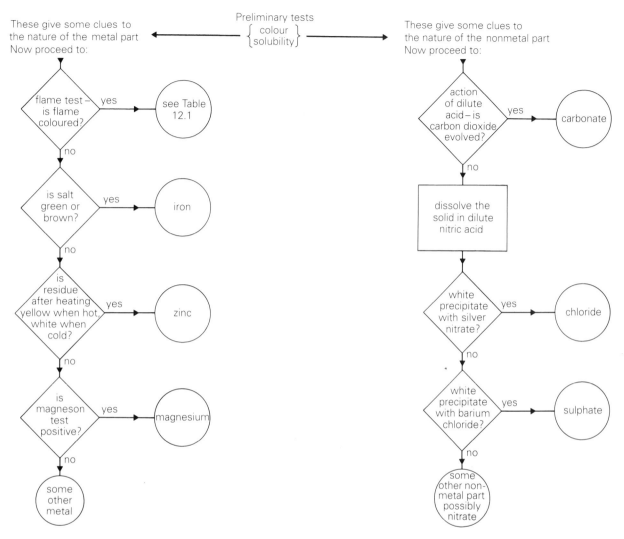

Table 12.2 A flow diagram for simple analysis.

12.6 Malachite

This green substance, which is found in rocks in central Africa, is said to be the **ore** of a common metal. (The ore of a metal is a compound of that metal which occurs naturally in the earth.) The analysis of crushed, purified malachite provides a good chance to use some of the chemistry we have studied up to now.

Experiment 12.2
Malachite investigation

Carry out the following experiments on a sample of malachite.

1 Observe the appearance of malachite.

Safety note

Malachite is harmful. Dilute sulphuric acid (0.5M to 2M) is irritant.

Safety note

Only your teacher should do this experiment.

Safety note

Hydrogen is explosive.

2 Place a spatula measure of malachite in a test-tube fitted with a bung and a glass tube. Dip the glass tube into a test-tube containing limewater (Fig 3.7). Heat the solid with a Bunsen burner. What changes do you observe? What does this tell you about malachite?

3 Add dilute sulphuric acid to a sample of malachite. Identify the gas which is given off. What is the solution which remains?

You have probably worked out by now that malachite is a compound of copper. Can you think of two ways of getting copper metal: one using the residue from step **2**, the other using the solution from step **3**? Discuss your plans with your teacher before carrying them out.

These tests tell us a lot about malachite. We see clearly that the nonmetal part is carbonate since carbon dioxide is given off on heating and on the addition of acid.

The metal part is probably copper, as the colours blue and green indicate. More tests can be done to make sure of this. The flame test gives a blue-green colour which again indicates copper. How can copper be extracted from the solid to make certain? There are at least four ways of doing this:

1 Reduction with carbon
The black solid which remains after heating is probably copper oxide and this can be reduced with powdered carbon (charcoal) by heating in a test-tube. Brown copper can be seen at the end (Section 10.4).

2 Reduction with hydrogen
The black solid can also be reduced using hydrogen (Section 10.6). Since water, the other product, is given off as a vapour, the copper which remains can be tested to show that it conducts electricity.

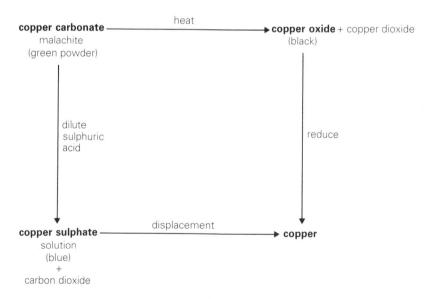

Table 12.3 The reactions of malachite.

3 Displacement with iron

The solution which remains after the addition of sulphuric acid is copper sulphate solution. If we dip an iron nail into this it will *displace* copper from the solution (Section 10.7) and become coated brown.

4 Electrolysis

The blue solution can also be electrolysed and copper is deposited at the cathode (Chapter 13).

The reactions of malachite are summarized in Table 12.3.

Questions

1 The ore, chalcanthite, is blue. It dissolves in water and in acids. It does not fizz with acids.
    a When an iron nail is dropped into a chalcanthite solution, the nail goes red-brown. Which metal does chalcanthite contain?
    b If chalcanthite does *not* fizz with acids, which 'nonmetal part' does it not contain?
    c Chalcanthite solution forms a white precipitate with acidified barium chloride solution. Which 'nonmetal part' does chalcanthite contain?
    d What is the chemical name of chalcanthite?
    e Chalcanthite can be found at Rio Tinto in Spain. Do you think it is likely that it is found at the surface or is it found underground? Give a reason for your answer.

2 At the Strassfurt salt mines in Germany, large deposits of sylvite are found. Sylvite is white and it dissolves in water.
    a Sylvite gives a lilac flame. Which metal does it contain?
    b Sylvite does not fizz with acids nor does its solution form a precipitate with acidified barium chloride solution. Which 'nonmetal parts' does sylvite *not* contain?
    c Sylvite solution forms a white precipitate with acidified silver nitrate solution. What 'nonmetal part' does sylvite contain?
    d What is the chemical name of sylvite?

3 A small sample of a powdered mineral was heated strongly (in the absence of air) in a hard glass test-tube fitted with a delivery tube dipping into limewater. The limewater soon turned milky. A black solid formed in the test-tube, it dissolved in dilute sulphuric acid giving a pale blue solution which gradually lost its colour when a weighed iron nail was dipped into it. Meanwhile, a pink deposit formed on the iron nail.
    a Name three elements that are certainly present in the mineral.
    b What two elements are likely to be present in the black solid?
    c Why do you think the blue solution lost its colour?
    d If the pink deposit were scraped off the nail and the latter reweighed, would you expect any change in weight? If so, would you expect an increase or a decrease?

e How would you attempt to turn the pink deposit back to the black solid?

4 The white ore, witherite, fizzes when dilute hydrochloric acid is added to it. A gas is given off which turns limewater milky.
a What is the gas?
b What is the 'nonmetal part' in witherite?
c A flame test on witherite produces an apple-green flame. What is the 'metal part' in witherite?
d What is the chemical name of witherite?
e After witherite is treated with dilute hydrochloric acid, the solution forms a white precipitate when sulphuric acid is added. What is this precipitate? (This last part is difficult.)

5 When a sample of clear sea water is evaporated, different crystals form at different stages of the evaporation.

	Amount of evaporation	Metal part tests	Nonmetal part tests
P	0–60 %	red flame	carbon dioxide with acid
Q	80–85 %	red flame	white solid with barium chloride
R	90–95 %	intense yellow flame	white solid with silver nitrate
S	98–99 %	no flame, but blue solid with magneson 1	white solid with barium chloride

a What are the four salts P, Q, R and S?
b Of the four which is the most soluble in water and which the least?
c The amount of R in the sea far exceeds the amount of the other salts together. Does this surprise you?
d The solution that remains after 99 % evaporation gives a lilac flame colour. What does this tell you?
e Some seas evaporate and then salt deposits form. Different salts often occur in different places on the old sea bed. Suggest a reason for this.

6 25 cm^3 each of samples of different sorts of water were added to beakers. The samples were then evaporated to dryness. The solid that was left in each beaker was then weighed.

Type of water	Mass of beaker	Mass of beaker and solid left after evaporation
sea water	22.75 g	23.67 g
'hard' tap water	23.08 g	23.19 g
'softened' tap water	21.90 g	21.99 g
'deionized' water	22.44 g	22.44 g

a How much solid was left in each case?
b How pure do you think 'deionized' water is?
c Is 'softened' tap water pure? Give a reason for your answer.
d How much solid would you expect to get if you evaporated distilled water?
e How much solid would you expect to get if you evaporated rain water?

7 (Difficult) A blue solid A gives off steam and two other gases when heated. They are B, a brown acidic gas, and C, a colourless gas which relights a glowing splint. A black residue D remains after heating. When D is added to nitric acid, a blue solution of A is obtained. An iron nail placed in this solution soon becomes coated with a brown substance E.
a Identify the gas C.
b What can you say about the black solid D knowing that it reacts with nitric acid as stated?
c What can you say about the compound A knowing that it is formed by the action of nitric acid on D?
d State, with reasons, the elements you think are present in the gas B.
e State, with reasons, the nature of E and explain how it is formed.
f Name A and show the above reactions in the form of a flow diagram.

Chapter 13

Electricity in the manufacture of chemicals

In Chapter 11 we saw how metals in the middle of the affinity series were manufactured by reduction of their oxide ores – often using carbon. More reactive metals cannot easily be produced by reduction and so *electrolysis* is used. This is the theme of this chapter and it will enable you to understand how reactive metals (and nonmetals) are produced from their ores.

13.1 Which substances conduct electricity?

To test whether substances conduct electricity we need an electrical circuit. This must contain a **power supply** (battery or powerpack up to 6V), a means of detecting whether a **current** is flowing (ammeter or light bulb) and the sample, all joined by wires. This is represented in Fig 13.1. If the sample conducts well enough, the bulb will light.

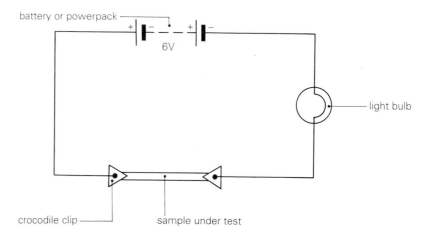

Fig 13.1 Testing the conductivity of a solid.

Solids can be tested by fastening the clips on to either side of a lump of material. As we saw in Chapter 8, metals and carbon conduct electricity. Nonmetals and solids which are compounds do not.

Liquids and *solutions* can be tested by dipping a pair of carbon rods into them (Fig 13.2). It is found that no pure substances which are liquids at room temperature conduct electricity (with the exception of the liquid metal, mercury). It may come as a surprise to you to discover that pure water is a poor conductor. However, many *solutions* conduct, and water, as it occurs in nature, is seldom very pure.

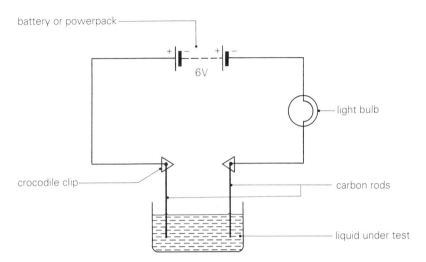

Fig 13.2 Testing the conductivity of a liquid or a solution.

Chlorine is toxic. Use a fume cupboard.

Iodine is harmful.

It is found that solutions in water of *salts, acids* and *alkalis* conduct electricity. Solutions in water of other substances, such as ethanol or sugar do not conduct. When the carbon rods are dipped into solutions which do conduct, bubbling is seen. The solutions are being broken down by the electric current, a process called **electrolysis.**

Molten salts also conduct electricity and this can be shown by melting the salt in a crucible and dipping in the carbon rods. It is just possible to melt calcium chloride and potassium iodide with a good Bunsen in order to try this. Again the electric current **decomposes** the salts to their elements (brown iodine is seen, for example, when potassium iodide conducts). We shall investigate the products of the decomposition in the next section.

We have seen that metals conduct without being broken down, but all other substances which conduct decompose as they do so. These are called **electrolytes** and are said to undergo electrolysis when a current passes through them.

Summary

Solids   metals and carbon conduct (without electrolysis)
               other solids do not conduct
Liquids   molten metals conduct (without electrolysis)
               molten salts are electrolytes
               other pure liquids do not conduct
Solutions solutions of salts, acids and alkalis are electrolytes
               other solutions do not conduct

13.2 Electrolysis of molten salts

First we must consider the carbon rods, which are called **electrodes**. The positive electrode (attached to the positive terminal of the power supply) is called the **anode** and the negative electrode is called the **cathode**.

Fig 13.3 The electrolysis of molten lead bromide.

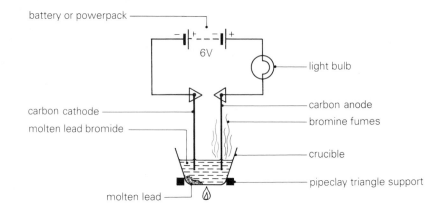

battery or powerpack

6V

light bulb

carbon cathode

carbon anode

molten lead bromide

bromine fumes

crucible

pipeclay triangle support

molten lead

Safety note

This must be carried out in a fume cupboard. Lead vapour and bromine are toxic.

Table 13.1 Electrolysis of two molten salts.

Lead bromide is a salt which is easily melted. If the apparatus shown in Fig 13.3 is used to electrolyse the molten salt, a small metallic globule is seen at the cathode and brown fumes at the anode. The metallic globule is lead and the brown fumes are bromine. Thus the compound lead bromide has been broken down into its elements by the electric current. Some results for other similar electrolytes are shown in Table 13.1.

When molten salts are electrolysed the *metal* is released at the *cathode* and the *nonmetal* at the *anode*.

Substance	Cathode product	Anode product
molten sodium chloride	sodium (hard to see)	chlorine (smell, bleaches pH paper)
molten potassium iodide	potassium (hard to see)	iodine (brown colour, purple vapour)

Background Reading

Sir Humphry Davy (1778–1829)

Davy was born in Cornwall and was reported to have been rather idle at school! His interest in chemistry possibly sprang from his first job as apprentice to a local surgeon.

In 1801 he moved to the Royal Institution in London where he soon became popular for his chemistry lectures. He constructed a battery at the Royal Institution which he used to electrolyse many substances. In 1807 he tried molten 'caustic potash' (potassium hydroxide). He obtained a small metallic globule, which he realised must be a new element. He called this potassium and

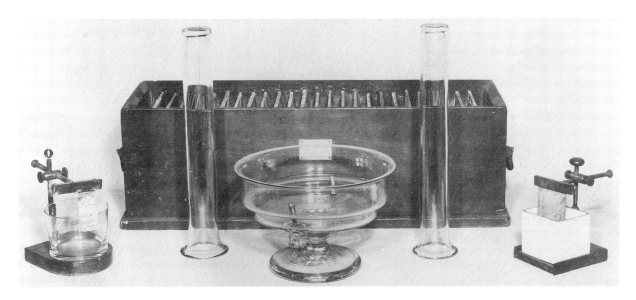

Fig 13.4 Sir Humphry Davy's apparatus for his electrolysis experiments.

described his discovery as 'A capital experiment!'. He went on to discover sodium, and later barium, strontium, calcium and magnesium. He was a prolific experimenter and he also invented a miners' safety lamp.

Questions

1 Why could Davy not have electrolysed potassium hydroxide solution to get potassium?

2 Name possible electrolytes from which Davy could have obtained sodium and magnesium.

13.3 Electrolysis of solutions

In Section 13.1 it was stated that bubbles were seen at the electrodes when solutions conducted electricity. Therefore we need an apparatus in which we can collect any gases formed at the electrodes when solutions are electrolysed (see Fig 13.5 overleaf). Some typical results from this experiment are shown in Table 13.2. (Do not do this experiment in class.)

Table 13.2 Electrolysis of some solutions.

Substance	Cathode product	Anode product
copper chloride solution	copper (brown 'plating')	chlorine (green gas, smell)
lead nitrate solution	lead (metallic crystals)	oxygen (often hard to identify)[*]
potassium iodide solution	hydrogen ('pop' test)	iodine (gives a brown solution)
magnesium bromide solution	hydrogen ('pop' test)	bromine (gives a brown solution)
sodium sulphate solution	hydrogen ('pop' test)	oxygen (often hard to identify)[*]
dilute sulphuric acid (hydrogen sulphate solution)	hydrogen ('pop' test)	oxygen (often hard to identify)[*]

[*]If the electrode is made of carbon, the oxygen can react to produce carbon dioxide.

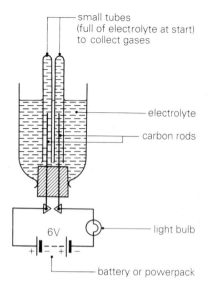

small tubes
(full of electrolyte at start)
to collect gases

— electrolyte

— carbon rods

6V

— light bulb

— battery or powerpack

Fig 13.5 The electrolysis of solutions.

There are some surprises here. Instead of metals at the cathode we sometimes get hydrogen. Except in the case of the dilute acid (which itself contains hydrogen), this must be coming from the water (hydrogen oxide). It can also be seen that metals high in the affinity series (see Chapter 10) are not deposited, whereas metals lower down are deposited.

At the anode we get the nonmetal if this is chlorine, bromine or iodine; but we do not get sulphur or its compounds from sulphate, nor do we get nitrogen or its compounds from nitrate. Instead we get oxygen from the water. Here is a summary of the results of the electrolysis of solutions:

product at cathode *either* the metal from the salt, *or* hydrogen (from the water) if the metal is high in the affinity series;

product at anode chlorine, bromine or iodine if they are present, otherwise oxygen from the water.

Safety note

Take great care when investigating unknown products. Do not run these cells for long if bromine (corrosive) or chlorine (toxic) is produced at the anode.

13.4 Electroplating

The fact that some metals (those which are low in the affinity series) are deposited on the cathode is useful in **electroplating**, a very important technique in industry.

If a battery like that in Fig 13.6 is set up to electroylse copper sulphate solution using *copper* electrodes, nothing much seems to happen when the current is switched on. We would expect copper to be produced at the cathode and a deposit of pink copper can be seen there when the electrode is removed from the solution. We might well expect oxygen at the anode, but there are clearly no bubbles. If we were to weigh the plates before and after the experiment we would find that:

loss of mass of the anode = gain in mass of the cathode

(After the experiment the plates need to be washed carefully with water, then with a volatile liquid like propanone and left to dry in the air.) The anode loses copper to the solution and the cathode gains an equal amount. The blue colour of the solution remains the same which confirms that this is happening.

This set-up is useful in purifying copper. Impure copper is made the anode in an electrolysis cell with copper sulphate solution as the electrolyte (Fig 13.7). Copper leaves the anode and is *plated* on to the cathode. The impurities either stay on the anode or

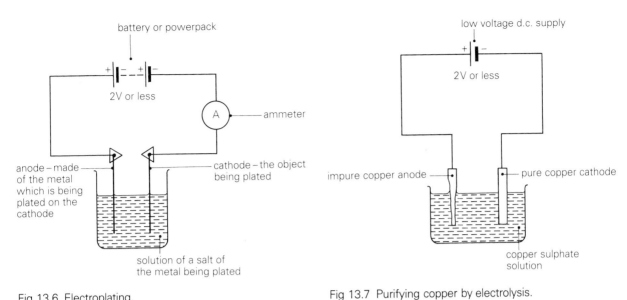

Fig 13.6 Electroplating.

Fig 13.7 Purifying copper by electrolysis.

Safety note

Only use the solutions that your teacher gives you for electroplating.

form a sludge in the bottom of the tank, but they do not plate the cathode. The plated copper is 99.9 % pure.

It is possible to do simple electroplating yourself using a circuit as shown in Fig 13.6. To ensure that the plating is even the current must be kept low, or, more exactly the ratio

$$\frac{current}{area\ of\ object}$$

must be kept low. The object to be plated must be clean and free from grease. Ideally, special salts should be used. Copper and brass objects can be plated with nickel or zinc using this method.

Electroplating is widely used in the manufacture of metal objects as it enables a thin layer of expensive metal to be plated on to a cheaper base metal. For example, 'silver' cutlery which is marked 'EPNS' (electroplated nickel silver) has a layer of silver plated on to an alloy of copper, nickel and zinc. Many steel objects, such as car bumpers, are electroplated with chromium to improve their appearance and to stop corrosion.

13.5 Obtaining metals by electrolysis

While metals such as iron and zinc can be made by the chemical reduction of their ores, metals such as sodium and aluminium have to be made by electrolysis. Sodium is made by the electrolysis of sodium chloride. This must be molten rather than in solution, if sodium metal is to be produced. Molten sodium

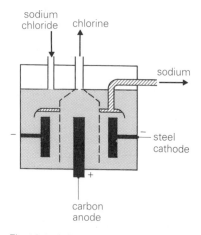

Fig 13.8 A Down's cell.

chloride is electrolysed in a Down's cell (Fig 13.8), calcium chloride being added to lower the melting point. Chlorine, a useful nonmetal, is produced at the anode and must be kept apart from the molten sodium which comes off at the cathode. In this country the sodium chloride is mined from the vast deposits under Cheshire and the industry is situated there. Sodium can be used to produce metals like titanium by reduction of their molten chlorides.

Aluminium is another metal made by the electrolysis of its molten compounds. The ore is called *bauxite* and is imported from Australia, Guinea and other countries. Bauxite needs treatment to produce the *alumina* (aluminium oxide) which is used to make aluminium. The alumina is mixed with other compounds to lower its melting point and then electrolysed when molten (Fig 13.9). The aluminium produced has a wide variety of uses since it is light, strong, hardwearing and a good conductor of electricity. Its uses range from kitchen foil to aeroplane construction. Aluminium is expensive as electricity is needed to produce it. In many countries, aluminium plants are sited where the electricity supply is cheapest, often near hydroelectric power plants. Aluminium manufacture is described as an 'energy based industry' as keeping down the cost of electrical energy is more important than reducing the transport costs of the ore. Less electrical energy is used in the manufacture of chemicals from sodium chloride so it is cheaper to build the factory near the deposits themselves. This is an example of a 'raw-material based' industry.

Fig 13.9 An aluminium cell.

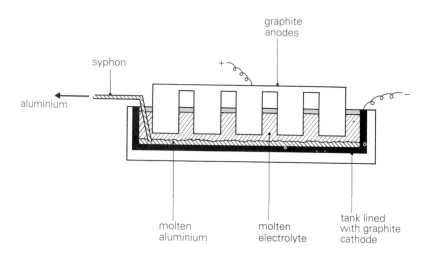

13.6 Obtaining nonmetals by electrolysis

Of the nonmetals, the most reactive is fluorine which comes off at the anode when a mixture of hydrogen fluoride and molten potassium fluoride is electrolysed. Fluorine is such a reactive gas that many common substances catch fire when they come into contact with it. It is not surprising that very little fluorine is made.

On the other hand, almost a million tonnes of chlorine, the second most reactive nonmetal, are manufactured in the UK each year. Once again the electrolyte is sodium chloride, but this time it can be in solution. This is mined from the Cheshire salt deposits by pumping down water to dissolve the salt as *brine* and then pumping this up again. When the solution is electrolysed, chlorine is produced at the anode, hydrogen at the cathode and sodium hydroxide is left behind (see Fig 13.10 below):

$$\text{sodium chloride} + \underset{\text{(water)}}{\text{hydrogen hydroxide}} \xrightarrow{\text{(electrolysis)}} \text{chlorine} + \text{hydrogen} + \text{sodium hydroxide}$$

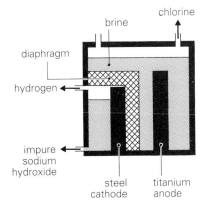

Fig 13.10 Electrolysis of brine in a diaphragm cell.

There are three useful products here:
The hydrogen produced by this process is used largely to make margarine, though the biggest overall use of hydrogen is to make ammonia for fertilizers.
Sodium hydroxide is used to make other alkalis, fibres and paper.
Chlorine is now the most important of the three and can be used to make a wide variety of products (see page 165).

13.7 The particles involved in electrolysis

When a substance is electrolysed, some particles move to the negative cathode. Since 'unlike charges attract' (see *Physics 11–14* page 196), the particles moving towards the cathode will be positively charged. Similarly, negatively charged particles are attracted to the anode. These charged particles are called *ions*.

Metals form positive ions.
Nonmetals form negative ions.

In a solid salt, the negative and positive ions attract one another and are held in a rigid regular structure. They can only vibrate (move sideways or up and down slightly). When the salt is melted or dissolved, the ions become free to move around. If charged electrodes are present, electrolysis will then occur, the ions moving to the electrode with the opposite charge.

Further reading

For further reading on electrolysis, see *Physics 11–14* pages 199–201.

Summary

1 Electrolytes decompose when they conduct electricity.

2 Molten salts and solutions of acids, alkalis and salts are electrolytes.

3 When a molten metal salt is electrolysed:
At the cathode the metal is produced.
At the anode the nonmetal is produced.

4 When a solution is electrolysed, the products are:
At the cathode: either the metal (if it is low in the affinity series) or hydrogen.
At the anode: chlorine, bromine or iodine if these are present, otherwise oxygen.

5 A metal object can be electroplated if it is made the cathode of a cell which has the plating metal as the anode.

6 Reactive metals and nonmetals are made from their ores by electrolysis.

7 Electrolytes consist of charged particles called *ions* which move freely when the salt is molten or dissolved. Then they are attracted to the electrode of opposite charge.

Questions

1 Of the following which are good and which are very poor conductors?

a	Copper.	**i**	Sugar solution.
b	Iron.	**j**	Dilute sulphuric acid.
c	Plastic.	**k**	Solid sodium chloride.
d	Glass.	**l**	Molten sodium chloride.
e	Carbon (graphite).	**m**	Sodium chloride solution.
f	Water.	**n**	Copper sulphate crystals.
g	Ethanol.	**o**	Copper sulphate solution.
h	Mercury.		

2 a What is the difference between a conductor and an electrolyte?
b In Question 1, which of the conductors also behave as electrolytes?

3 a Draw a diagram to show how you would electrolyse a molten salt. Label the electrodes and the electrolyte.
b What products would you expect at the cathode and the anode if you electrolysed:
(i) Molten sodium bromide?
(ii) Molten calcium chloride?
(iii) Molten lead iodide?

4 When sodium chloride solution is electrolysed, hydrogen is obtained at the cathode and chlorine at the anode.
  a Where does the hydrogen come from?
  b How would you test for the hydrogen?
  c Suggest why sodium is *not* formed at the cathode.
  d What else might have been obtained at the anode?
  e Sketch a diagram of the apparatus you would use to collect the chlorine and hydrogen gases during electrolysis.

5 a Why does the electrolysis of copper sulphate solution produce copper at the cathode while potassium sulphate solution gives hydrogen at the cathode?
  b What would you expect to get at the cathode if silver nitrate solution were electrolysed?
  c What would you expect at the cathode if magnesium sulphate solution were electrolysed?

6 Write down the products you would expect at the cathode and anode when the following are electrolysed:
  a Molten potassium chloride.
  b Potassium chloride solution.
  c Sodium sulphate solution.
  d Dilute hydrochloric acid.
  e Copper nitrate solution.

7 When malachite reacts with sulphuric acid, a blue solution is produced (Section 12.6). One way of showing that this is a copper salt is to obtain copper from it by electrolysis.
  a Draw a diagram of the apparatus you would use for this experiment.
  b Where would you find copper?
  c What other substance would be produced during the electrolysis?
  d When limestone reacts with hydrochloric acid, a colourless solution is produced. What products are formed at the anode and cathode when this solution is electrolysed?

8 Name a metal which:
  a Occurs naturally as a pure element.
  b Is normally obtained using electrolysis.
  c Is normally obtained by heating its oxide with carbon.

9 a Tin is found in tinstone (cassiterite, tin oxide) in Cornwall. Refer to Section 10.7 and then suggest how tin is made from tinstone.
  b Sodium is found as rock salt (sodium chloride) in Cheshire. Suggest how sodium is obtained from rock salt.

10 Overleaf are the results of electrolysing some molten solids in a fume cupboard.
  a What are the products of electrolysing molten lead iodide:
    (i) at the cathode
    (ii) at the anode
    Explain your answers.

Substance	Seen at cathode	Cathode product	Seen at anode	Anode product
molten sodium chloride	flashes of light	sodium	gas which bleaches pH paper	chlorine
molten lead iodide	small metallic bead		brown colour, purple fumes	
molten X	small metallic bead		brown vapour bleaches pH paper	

b Identify the elements formed at the cathode and the anode when molten X is electrolysed. Identify X.

c Describe what you might expect to see at the anode and the cathode when molten potassium iodide is electrolysed.

11 Here are the results of attempting to pass electricity through a variety of substances.

Substance	Does it conduct?	Anode product	Cathode product
A	no	—	—
B	yes	none	none
C	yes	chlorine	hydrogen
D	yes	oxygen	copper

Which substance could be:

a pure water
b sodium chloride solution
c copper
d glass

e copper sulphate crystals
f copper sulphate solution
g hydrochloric acid
h a carbon rod?

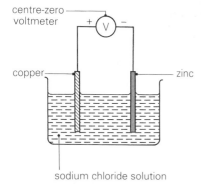

centre-zero voltmeter

copper

zinc

sodium chloride solution

Fig 13.11 An experiment to establish the electrochemical series.

Additional material

Electricity from chemical reactions

If a piece of copper and a piece of zinc are dipped in sodium chloride solution and connected up to a centre-zero voltmeter (Fig 13.11) a voltage is produced. If the zinc is replaced by magnesium, a larger voltage is produced on the same side of the zero. If the magnesium is now replaced by silver, the voltage changes to the other side of the zero. Two pieces of copper, of

magnesium	−1.2 volts
zinc	−0.7 volts
iron	−0.3 volts
tin	−0.2 volts
copper	0
silver	+0.2 volts

Table 13.3 Some typical results when metals are paired with copper.

course, produce no voltage. Table 13.3 shows some typical results when various metals are paired with copper in this experiment.

If another metal is substituted for the copper, the voltage will be the difference between the readings in the table. For example, magnesium and zinc should produce about 0.5 volts and magnesium and silver should produce about 1.4 volts.

The order of the metals in Table 13.3 is called the **electrochemical series**; you will notice that the metals shown are in the same order as in the affinity and displacement series (Chapter 10). The electrical measurements can be made very accurately and the electrochemical series can be used to separate metals which are very close in the displacement series. For example, nickel is found to be above tin.

The electrical energy comes from chemical reactions. This can be seen in the Daniell cell[*] (Fig 13.12a) which gives a voltage of 1.1 V. After the cell has been in use for a while the appearance of the zinc rod makes it clear that some zinc has reacted. If the copper can were dried and reweighed it would be found to have gained mass. The reaction which supplies the electrical energy here is:

zinc + copper sulphate ⟶ copper + zinc sulphate

Fig 13.12 (a) A Daniell cell (b) Appearance of zinc rod after cell has been in use for a while.

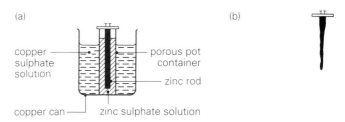

All batteries used in everyday life convert chemical energy into electrical energy. However, the chemical reactions which occur are often complicated. One of the commonest cells is the 'dry cell' (Fig 13.13). Here the chemical reaction is between zinc and manganese dioxide. The electrolyte is in the form of a paste, hence the cell is described as 'dry'.

Car batteries depend on the reaction of lead with brown lead oxide in the presence of sulphuric acid. The reaction may be reversed by forcing electricity back through the battery which means that the battery can be recharged, a most important point. Rechargeable batteries are sometimes known as **accumulators.**

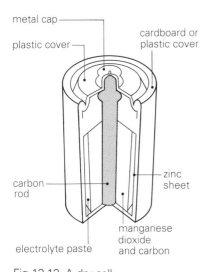

Fig 13.13 A dry cell.

[*]A *cell* has just one pair of electrodes (for example zinc and copper in a Daniell cell). A *battery* consists of a number of cells joined together (see *Physics 11–14* page 146).

Chapter 14

Chemicals from raw materials

14.1 Where do chemicals come from?

The raw materials of chemistry mentioned before in this book are summarized below:

Air (Chapter 4)
Oxygen, nitrogen and other gases are separated by fractional distillation of liquid air.

Water (Chapter 7)
This is a source of hydrogen (by electrolysis) as well as dissolved salts. Water is also used as a coolant and solvent in the chemical industry.

Rocks (Chapter 9)
Some rocks are useful as they are (for example, limestone). Others contain minerals from which metals and nonmetals can be obtained (Chapters 9 and 13).

Living things
Starch can be fermented to make ethanol, the source of many important materials (Section 5.4). The starch can be obtained from cereal crops (such as wheat and rye) and potatoes.

Fossil fuels
Coal, oil and natural gas come from the fossilised remains of plants and animals. From oil come many important chemicals such as lubricants and plastics (Section 2.4). Coal provides medicines and dyes among many other products.

Background Reading

Fossil fuels

Crude oil is thought to have been made from the bodies of small sea creatures compressed in sedimentary rocks. Oil is found absorbed in porous rocks (Fig 14.1). Similarly coal was formed from the remains of rotting trees which have become covered and subjected to pressure over hundreds of millions of years. (Sometimes fossilised plants are found in lumps of coal.) Natural gas was formed at the same time as the coal. It escaped upwards until trapped by solid rock.

Fig 14.1.

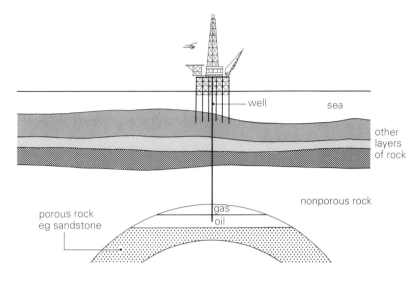

Fig 14.2 An oil platform in the North Sea.

The hazards of mining fossil fuels

You know that oil and natural gas are found in various parts of the world – for example America, the Middle East and the North Sea. They are removed from the ground by drilling wells. When the wells are at sea there are hazards from wild winds and massive waves. The men who work aboard these rigs are well paid, it is true, but they risk their lives to extract the oil for us.

Coal is dug from open cast mines when it is near the surface. This is relatively safe but it leaves great scars on the landscape. Other coal is dug from deep pits which are dangerous for the miners who work there.

14.2 What does the chemical industry do?

Many of the everyday substances we take for granted are manufactured from the raw materials mentioned in the previous section. These range from medicines to plastics, from fuels to paints, from detergents to metals; the list is vast.

In making these many products, the chemical industry is bound to cause some pollution and we must balance our need for manufactured articles against this. We *could* eliminate the pollution, but only by making the products very expensive indeed. Society has to decide how much pollution is acceptable.

Mines and quarries have to be built in more and more areas as a result of the need for more raw materials. In your parents' lifetime, industry was smaller and could cope fairly easily. However, the world's population has increased and that population wants an increasing number of material things. This puts a heavier demand on the chemical industry and it has to work hard to avoid causing yet more pollution and more damage to the landscape.

14.3 Recycling

Some raw materials are replaceable (trees for making paper, for example) but we are using them so fast it is hard to keep up. Fossil fuels and minerals are made so slowly that we will run out of them eventually (Fig 14.3).

Fig 14.3.

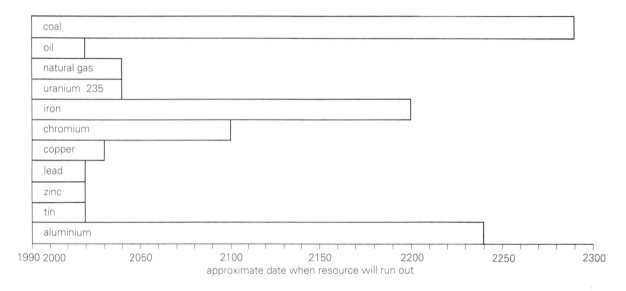

approximate date when resource will run out

This points to a need to recycle materials where we can. Also, disposing of our waste is expensive in itself. Everyday, a long goods train goes to a site in the home counties carrying London's household waste. This is buried in landfill sites. Fortunately, much is degradable (it corrodes) or biodegradable (bacteria rot it). Unfortunately most plastics are not broken down in either of these ways.

The contents of a typical dustbin are shown in Table 14.1. You might like to check the contents of your family dustbin to compare its composition (see Fig 14.4). Wear rubber gloves and

Table 14.1 Contents of an average dustbin.

Amount	Product	Description	Possible uses
40 %	combustibles	paper, plastic film, textiles	fuel or making board
20 %	'rottable' material	vegetable, animal and food waste, wood	make methane or animal feedstock
15 %	small particles	dust, dirt, ash, grit	use as landfill
6 %	glass	mainly white but some green and brown	bottle manufacture
5 %	tin-plate	tin cans (tin-plated steel) plus labels and traces of contents	detinning to recover tin and steel
1%	iron	discarded household goods	recycling to steel
<1 %	other metals	aluminium, some zinc and copper	processes for recycling these are under development

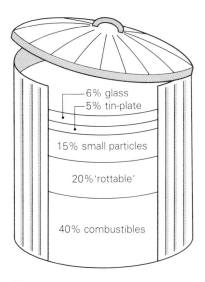

Fig 14.4.

- 6% glass
- 5% tin-plate
- 15% small particles
- 20% 'rottable'
- 40% combustibles

ask your parents' permission. You can see that many of the items can be recycled or reclaimed (used for something different). However, it is often cheaper to bury or burn the rubbish. Then it is necessary to manufacture the article again. This may use up scarce raw materials and cause more pollution.

Substances which are recycled at the moment include:

Iron
This is easily picked out by a magnet. Many steelmaking furnaces run mainly on scrap iron.

Aluminium
This can be separated, melted down and recast.

Glass
Bottles are collected in bottle banks (Fig 14.5) and the 'cullet' (finely broken glass) is used to make new bottles.

Why do the bottles have to be broken though? Why can't they be recyled *as bottles* (which happens to milk bottles)? Supermarkets could easily collect empty drinks bottles as they do in France. All it requires is a bit of effort – effort on our behalf to return the bottles; effort on the supermarket's part to organise the collection. Recycling bottles would avoid mining more limestone and also save the energy needed to make glass. On the other hand, sterilizing the bottles does cost money.

Fig 14.5 Using a bottle bank.

14.4 What do we do when the oil runs out?

From Fig 14.3 you can see that crude oil will all be gone within your lifetime. Some ways of coping with this are:

Avoid using oil as a fuel
At present only 10 % of oil is used to make chemicals, the rest is burned. Replacement fuels are needed for:

a Transport (cars, planes and ships). *Hydrogen* could be used (see Fig 14.6). This could come from water by electrolysis, so an electric current would be needed. Alternatively, *methane*

Fig 14.6 A hydrogen car – note the hydrogen cylinders in the boot.

could be produced by the fermentation of such things as animal manure or garden waste. This is called biogas generation and a lot of research is going on in this area.

b Generating electrical energy. Some power stations are still fuelled by oil, though many are coal-fired. (Coal reserves are thought to be capable of lasting 200 years). Coal or nuclear fuel should be used for all power stations.

Look for more expensive sources of oil

Some oil is present in shales, mixed up with the small particles. Extracting it will be expensive, but the price of oil continues to rise and it will make it worthwhile when most of the other oil has gone. (This will be true for other minerals too. As they become scarcer, the price will rise and it will be economic to mine lower grade ores.)

Use alternative sources of chemicals

a Coal could be used to produce many substances we now get from oil.

b Fermentation of starch or sugars gives ethanol which can be made into plastics.

During your lifetime you should see a fascinating shift in the ways chemicals are produced – perhaps you will be involved in the research and development of these changes.

Summary

1 Chemical raw materials include air, water, rocks, fossil fuels and living things.

2 The chemical industry makes many things essential for modern life but it pollutes and destroys by its activities. These bad effects must be minimised.

3 Recycling helps to save raw materials and cuts down on pollution.

4 Oil is wasted if burned as a fuel: it is needed as a source of chemicals. When it runs out we shall need alternatives.

5 As minerals become scarcer, their price rises and lower-grade ores are worth extracting.

Questions

1 Some common sources of chemicals include:
A air **B** the Earth **F** fossil fuels **D** living things
E water.
Which source is chosen for the manufacture of the following?
a Argon.
b Ethanol for drinks.
c Hydrogen.
d Limestone.
e Magnesium.
f Oxygen.
g Petrol for cars.

2 Give a use for each of the substances mentioned in Question 1 once they have been manufactured.

3 State another useful substance (other than those included in Question 1) that can be made from each of the five sources given in Question 1.

4 Which of the manufacturing processes in Question 1 involve a chemical rather than a physical separation?

5 Chemicals can be made using the following types of chemical reaction:
A electrolysis **B** fermentation
C neutralization **D** reduction with carbon
E thermal decomposition.
Which could be used for each of the following:
a The manufacture of iron in a blast furnace.
b Manufacturing quicklime from limestone.
c Manufacturing chlorine.
d Making beer.
e Manufacturing aluminium.
f Heating cinnabar (mercury sulphide) to make mercury.
g Making industrial alcohol from sugar?

6 Fig 14.7 shows pictures of some chemical factories. Pick, with reasons, the one that is used to:
a Purify water.
b Make steel.
c Distil crude oil.
d Make chlorine from sodium chloride.

Fig 14.7.

1

2

3

4

7 Look at Table 14.2 which lists major pollutants.
   a Which types of pollution are caused mainly by:
      coal-fired power stations
      farming
      motor vehicles
      the chemical industry
      us in our homes?
   b Choose one of the pollutants you have mentioned and say how its amount could be reduced.

Table 14.2 Some major pollutants.

Pollutant	Sources	Some effects
Air		
oxides of sulphur	combustion of coal and oil	corrosion of metals and stone, acid rain, bronchitis
smoke	combustion	smog, black buildings, less photosynthesis, cancer
carbon dioxide	burning fuels	affects climate, greenhouse effect
CFCs (chlorofluorocarbons)	aerosol propellants	breaks down ozone layer (causes skin cancer)
nitrogen oxides	vehicle exhausts	smog, acid rain
Land		
radioactive waste	accidental leaks from nuclear reactors	cancer
heavy metals (eg Pb, Hg, Cd)	chemical works, lead from car exhausts	damage to nervous system and kidneys
pesticides like DDT	crop spraying	kills beneficial insects and birds
Water		
fertilizers	overuse	stagnant rivers and lakes
heavy metals	as for *Land*	as for *Land*
pesticides	as for *Land*	as for *Land*

8 Imagine the state of our present world if we were attacked by a plastic-eating virus from outer space. Write a story based on this idea.

9 Look at Table 14.1 which shows the contents of dustbins.
   a Which of this waste is nondegradable (that is, it will not rot if buried in the ground)? Give reasons for your answers.
   b Which of the waste is biodegradable (broken down by bacteria in the soil)?
   c Which of the waste products are most important to recycle and why?

10 Pieces of plastic are often seen littering the countryside around a waste-disposal site, but other waste in not visible. Why is this?

11 Here are two letters to a local newspaper in a town. Near the town a giant chemical company is planning to build a plant to make sulphuric acid. The raw materials are sulphur, water and oxygen. Sulphuric acid is used to make detergents, fertilizers, paints and plastics. Sulphur dioxide is sometimes released during the process.

Letter 1
Sir,
I urge fellow townspeople to unite against the scourge of this awful factory. It will produce smoke and fumes and pollute our water. And all for what? A dangerous acid that wil be a hazard in road tankers and is too corrosive for all but specialist use.
　　Join me to oppose the factory!
　　Yours,
　　A. Andrews

Letter 2
Sir,
I am writing to say how much we should welcome the chemical factory into the area. We are honoured that sulphuric acid, so important for our modern way of life and our enjoyment of leisure, should be made near us. Of course it won't pollute the atmosphere – chemists are far too clever these days! But it will employ a good many extra people from the town and this might stop them hanging about the streets.
　　Well done the Chemical Company.
　　Yours,
　　B. Brown

Suppose you also lived there. Write a letter to the newspaper stating your own views and commenting on the two letters.

12 How might you and some friends get together to mount a campaign to persuade your local supermarket to stock fizzy drinks in returnable bottles?

13 In an open pit mine in the USA, copper ore forms 0.63 % of the rock. In a Zambian underground copper mine, the copper ore forms 2.5 % of the rock.
  a Which is likely to be the cheaper mining operation per tonne of rock dug? Explain your answer.
  b How many tonnes of rock have to be mined in (i) the USA, (ii) Zambia, to get 1 tonne of copper ore?
  c Explain why the Zambian mine would probably not be worth operating if the copper ore only formed 0.63% of the rock there.

Chapter 15 The Periodic Table

15.1 Relative atomic mass

In Section 8.5 we have seen that the different elements are made up of minute particles called atoms. All the atoms of a particular element are the same (or very similar) and differ from the atoms of the other elements. Elements cannot be broken down into other substances.

Scientists have developed ways of discovering how small atoms are and how much they weigh. For example, 20 grams of carbon can be shown to contain 10^{24} (1 000 000 000 000 000 000 000 000) carbon atoms. The mass of a single atom is very small indeed. The atoms of different elements have different masses and these were related to the lightest atom, hydrogen.[†]

One atom of oxygen has been found to weigh sixteen times as much as one atom of hydrogen. Thus we say that the **relative atomic mass** (relative to hydrogen) of oxygen is 16, or we use the shorthand 'O = 16'. The expression 'relative atomic mass' is often shortened to RAM.

An atom of carbon weighs twelve times as much as an atom of hydrogen, so its relative atomic mass is 12 (or we write C = 12). An atom of nitrogen weighs 14 times as much as an atom of hydrogen so its relative atomic mass is 14 (N = 14) and so on. Relative atomic masses are given for some elements in Appendix 1 on page 173.

15.2 'Families' of elements

In Chapter 8 we saw how the elements could be classified into three groups: reactive metals, everyday metals and nonmetals. Chemists today use a more refined classification based on the ideas of a Russian called Mendeleef (1869). He arranged the elements in order of ascending RAM and noticed that there were similarities every so often. If we do the same with the elements which we know about today, the list looks like this for the first twenty elements:

H He* Li Be B C N O F Ne * Na Mg Al Si
P S Cl Ar * K Ca

You will notice that the noble gases helium, neon and argon have been starred. These occur at regular intervals. They are very

[†] The modern system uses the ^{12}C isotope as exactly 12 rather than hydrogen as exactly 1. Instruments called mass spectrometers can measure atomic masses very accurately.

similar chemically (Section 4.1) and can be described as a 'family'. Another family includes the very reactive metals lithium, sodium and potassium (Li, Na, K). You have met sodium and potassium before and seen how they react similarly with water (Chapter 10). More experiments on these elements are described in section 15.3.

Mendeleef had the idea of arranging these and other 'families' in vertical columns or **groups**. The first twenty elements are arranged like this:

```
(H)                                    He
Li   Be   B    C    N    O    F    Ne
Na   Mg   Al   Si   P    S    Cl   Ar
K    Ca
```

Hydrogen does not fit very well, but all the other elements show similarities with the other one or two in their group. Mendeleef described this repetition of properties as the **periodic law**.

The next sections describe some groups more fully, but for a more detailed account of the periodic classification see Section 15.6.

15.3 Group I – the alkali metals

This family group is listed on the left of the Periodic Table and is thus called Group I. From the information in Section 15.2 we would expect the elements to be similar. The three most common elements in this group are lithium, sodium and potassium. They are all very unusual metals for they have very low melting points, low densities and they are very soft. They can be cut easily but the freshly exposed surfaces tarnish very quickly.

This, and the fact that all three elements have to be kept under oil, indicates that they react vigorously with oxygen. They all form white oxides which dissolve in water to form alkaline solutions. This is why they are called 'alkali metals'. (Note that it is the oxides and hydroxides of these elements which are alkaline, not the metals themselves.) All the metals react with the gas chlorine to form white chlorides, for example sodium chloride, common salt.

The reactions of sodium and potassium with water have been mentioned in Section 10.5. Lithium reacts similiarly:

lithium + water ⟶ lithium hydroxide + hydrogen

They all give hydrogen and a soluble alkaline hydroxide. The rate of reaction with water varies. Lithium reacts most slowly (though still quite vigorously), sodium next, while potassium bursts into flame. This shows us another feature of a Periodic Table group. As well as *similarities* (e.g. all reacting with water) there are often *trends* (e.g. the reactivity with water increases as we go down the group). The general trend in Group I is that the elements become more reactive down the group. The reaction with water shows this, as does the rate of tarnishing of a cut surface in air, which is fastest with potassium and slowest with lithium.

15.4 Group II – the alkaline earth metals

This group contains the elements Be (beryllium), Mg (magnesium) and Ca (calcium). Beryllium is rare but you will have come across the elements calcium and magnesium. How do they compare with the elements in Group I? The resemblance might be described as that of distant cousins! Calcium reacts with cold water, but magnesium will only react very slowly (Section 10.5).

The elements are harder than those of Group I and have higher melting points. Their oxides are alkaline but only slightly soluble in water (hence their name **alkaline earths**). However, within the group there is a similarity of properties and also a trend – as with Group I they become more reactive as we go down the group.

The real difference between Groups I and II lies in the formulae of their compounds. For example, the chlorides of Group I are NaCl, KCl etc whereas those of Group II are $CaCl_2$, $MgCl_2$ etc. (see Section 15.8).

15.5 Group VII – the halogens

Safety note

Chlorine is toxic.

Safety note

Bromine is corrosive, and should only be handled in a fume cupboard by a teacher.

Safety note

Iodine is harmful.

The elements of Group VII are the nonmetals fluorine (F), chlorine (Cl), bromine (Br) and iodine (I). You have met them before in Chapter 13 as they can be made by electrolysing the salts which contain them. For example, fluorine is made by electrolysing molten potassium fluoride, KF, and chlorine is made by electrolysing sodium chloride solution, NaCl (Section 13.6).

At room temperature fluorine is a colourless gas, chlorine a pale green gas, bromine is a red-brown liquid and iodine is a dark purple solid. (This increase in melting point is a trend down the group.) They all react with a wide variety of metals forming salts – the word halogen means 'saltformer'. Other similarities are that the halogens all have a rasping smell **and are very poisonous**. Several of them bleach solutions of indicators and they all react with alkalis like sodium hydroxide. (The other similarity is in their formulae, e.g. NaCl, NaBr, NaI and $CaCl_2$, $CaBr_2$ and CaI_2.)

The main trend is one of reactivity. When reacted with metals, fluorine is the most reactive and iodine the least. Notice that this is the other way round from Groups I and II which have the most reactive elements at the bottom.

Background Reading

Uses of the halogens

The commonest halogen, chlorine, has been used for many years in the treatment of water and has contributed to the eradication of cholera and typhoid in Britain. The chlorine compound sodium chlorate(I) is the active agent in domestic bleach and it is used in the treatment of water in swimming pools. The largest use of chlorine, however, is in the manufacture of the plastic PVC (polyvinylchloride), followed by its use in solvents such as trichloroethane which is used for dry-cleaning (see page 7). Chlorine is also used in the manufacture of weedkillers, insecticides (e.g. BHC), refrigerants and dyes. Such a list could go on for a long time. See Fig 15.1 for some examples.

Fig 15.1 Some uses of chlorine.

Bromine is too dangerous to be used as the pure element and its main use is in the compound dibromoethane, a petrol additive. Bromine is also used as silver bromide, a photographic emulsion, and in a number of dyes and medicines, but the list is shorter than for chlorine.

Iodine is used as a disinfectant in treating cuts and many iodine compounds are also used medically. Sodium iodide is added to common salt in areas where there is not enough iodine in the diet.

Fluorine, the most reactive member of the group, is again too dangerous to be used as the element, but fluorides are often used in toothpastes as they help to prevent tooth decay. An important compound of fluorine is the plastic PTFE (polytetrafluoroethene) which is used in nonstick pans and situations where friction-free bearings are needed. Other compounds include hydrofluoric acid, used to etch glass, and various components of specialist fire extinguishers. It is also used in the common anaesthetic fluothane, $CF_3CHBrCl$, which involves the use of chlorine and bromine as well.

Questions

1 Why is the use of DDT now restricted in Britain?

2 What are the properties needed in a fire extinguisher?

15.6 The periodic classification

In Section 15.2 we only considered the first twenty elements. In order to keep the 'families' of elements together after this it is necessary to insert a block of elements as shown:

																	(H)									He

```
                                                              (H)                                          He
Li  Be                                                                            B   C   N   O   F   Ne
Na  Mg                                                                            Al  Si  P   S   Cl  Ar
K   Ca  Sc  Ti  V   Cr  Mn  Fe  Co  Ni  Cu  Zn    Ga  Ge  As  Se  Br  Kr
Rb  Sr
```

It was Mendeleef's genius to spot this. The elements within the block are called the **transition elements**. They are a bit like a 'horizontal group' as you will see. The rest of the table has vertical groups which show similarities and trends as we have discovered for Groups I, II and VII. The rows across are called periods and these always begin with an alkali metal and end with a noble gas. Mendeleef said that the properties of the elements showed a periodic variation with relative atomic mass, in other words there is a repetition of properties periodically (from time to time). Many scientific systems (e.g. pendulums) have regular periods, but the periods in the Periodic Table vary in length.

15.7 Sorting metals

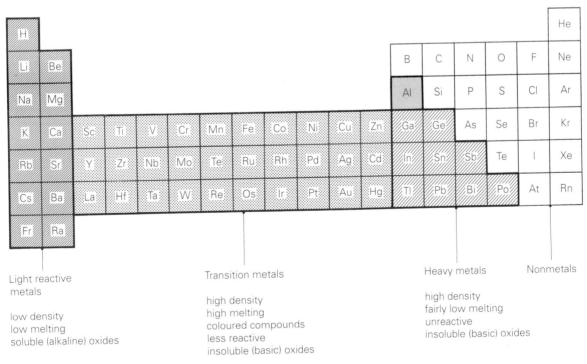

Light reactive metals

low density
low melting
soluble (alkaline) oxides

Transition metals

high density
high melting
coloured compounds
less reactive
insoluble (basic) oxides

Heavy metals

high density
fairly low melting
unreactive
insoluble (basic) oxides

Nonmetals

Fig 15.2 The regions of the Periodic Table.

In Chapter 8 we sorted metals into 'reactive' and 'everyday' metals. We can now see that most of the reactive metals are in Groups I and II of the Periodic Table. What about 'everyday metals'? These occur in one of two places – either in the transition metals or the 'heavy metals'. Fig 15.2 shows the main regions of the Periodic Table.

We have met many of the 'light' (low-density) reactive metals in Groups I and II. In the transition metals are found some of the commonest elements in everyday use – copper, iron, zinc, gold, silver and platinum. There is quite a variation within this set but many have coloured compounds (which makes the world, and the study of chemistry, a lot more interesting) and they are much less reactive but more structurally useful than the light reactive metals. Many of the heavy metals are rare, but tin and lead are well known. They are denser, softer and less reactive than many of the transition metals.

15.8 Formulae and the Periodic Table

Here are the formulae of some chlorides:

Group I	Group II	Group III	Group IV
NaCl	$MgCl_2$	$AlCl_3$	$SiCl_4$
KCl	$CaCl_2$	$GaCl_3$	$GeCl_4$
RbCl	$SrCl_2$		

You can see that there is a definite similarity of formulae within a group and a trend across a period.

The oxides follow a predictable pattern too:

Group I	Group II	Group III	Group IV	Group V	Group VI	Group VII
Na_2O	MgO	Al_2O_3	SiO_2	P_2O_5	SO_3	Cl_2O_7

The pattern here is that one atom of oxygen combines with two atoms of sodium, two atoms of oxygen with two atoms of magnesium, three atoms of oxygen with two atoms of aluminium etc. Such patterns do not always work well for elements on the right-hand side of the Periodic Table and there is little regularity in the formulae of transition metal compounds. Elsewhere in the classification, however, the formula of the oxide or chloride is often the most important way of assigning an element to a particular group.

Summary

1 When the elements are arranged in order of ascending atomic mass, their properties repeat in a regular manner. This is called the periodic law and leads to the Periodic Table.

2 Elements can be classified on the basis of similar properties into families called groups.

3 Different atoms have different masses. The relative atomic mass (RAM) of an element is the number of times one of its atoms is heavier than one atom of hydrogen.

4 Formulae show regular patterns in the Periodic Table.

Background Reading

The history of the Periodic Table

The first serious attempt to classify the chemical elements was made by the German scientist Döbereiner who noticed that sets of three very similar elements often had relative atomic masses such that the middle value was the average of the other two. He called such sets 'triads'. Examples included:

Li	7	Ca	40	Cl	35.5
Na	23	S	88	Br	80
K	39	Ba	137	I	127

In fact the atomic mass relationship occurs entirely by chance and not all the elements could be accounted for.

Fig 15.3 Mendeleef.

The next attempt came from the Englishman Newlands. In his system of 'octaves' he arranged the elements in order of increasing relative atomic mass in rows of seven so that the eighth element (octave) started a new row. The sequence started well but then became chaotic.

The Russian, Mendeleef, did much the same as Newlands but his understanding led him to realise that not all the elements had then been discovered so he left gaps for them: he also predicted the properties of these elements and it was the excellent agreement between his predictions and the properties of gallium and germanium when they were discovered in the 1870s that led to the acceptance of the Periodic Table in much the same form that it is still used today.

Questions

1 Can you find any other examples of Döbereiner triads?

2 Why, in 1863, did Newlands have every eighth rather than every ninth element starting a new row (as we see at the start of a modern Periodic Table)?

Questions

1 Place the following elements in their correct group in the Periodic Table, giving your reasons (the letters are *not* the symbols for the elements):

A A silvery element that conducts electricity and burns with a bright light to form a sparingly soluble oxide (pH = 9).

B A grey element that reacts violently with water to give a strongly alkaline solution (pH = 14).

C A gas that forms no chemical compound.

D A grey element that forms two chlorides one of them giving a green solution, the other a brown solution.

E A gas giving an acidic bleaching solution in water.

2 Place the following elements in the correct group in the Periodic Table, giving your reasons (the letters are *not* the symbols for the elements):

A A grey element which reacts with cold water and forms a chloride ACl_2.

B A dense, high melting element which conducts electricity and forms a brown chloride BCl_3.

C A dense element which is soft and malleable with a relatively low melting point. It forms an oxide CO_2.

D A red-purple solid which does not conduct electricity and burns vigorously in air to give a white acidic oxide D_2O_5.

3 a Consider the element calcium: list the properties for which it *might* be considered to be a Group I element and also the properties which show it is really a Group II element.

b List the properties of sodium which might tempt you to consider it as a Group II element and those which show it is really a Group I element.

4 Chlorine water is colourless; bromine water is yellow; iodine solution is red-brown.

	Final colour of solution
(i) chlorine water + potassium bromide	yellow
(ii) chlorine water + potassium iodide	red-brown
(iii) bromine water + potassium chloride	yellow
(iv) bromine water + potassium iodide	red-brown
(v) iodine solution + potassium chloride	red-brown
(vi) iodine solution + potassium bromide	red-brown

a In which three cases has there been a reaction?
b Write a word equation for one of the reactions in **a**.
c Which of the halogens is the most reactive?
Explain your answer.

5 A scientist has a grey element which is in Group I, Group II, the transition metals or is iodine. Devise a sequence of tests the scientist could use to classify the elements as quickly as possible.

6 Here are some formulae of the chlorides and oxides of elements in the first short period of the Periodic Table, lithium to fluorine:

$LiCl$ $BeCl_2$ CCl_4 NCl_3
Li_2O B_2O_3

Giving reasons *predict* formulae for:
a the oxide of beryllium (Be)
b the chloride of boron (B)
c the oxide of carbon (C)
d the oxide of nitrogen (N)
e the oxide of aluminium (Al)

Explorations 3

  Always discuss your plans with your teacher before starting any practical work

 Safety note

Hydrochloric acid is harmful at concentrations of 4 M or greater.

N A chemical company wants to make a metal road tanker which can be used to carry laboratory hydrochloric acid. Experiment (and look up data) to find which metal you would recommend.

O 'Tin cans' are made of thin steel sheet with a layer of tin plated onto it. Discover whether tin cans rust faster or slower than untreated steel (an 'iron' nail). What happens if the tin can is scratched right through the layer of tin?
What happens if the nail is galvanised (covered in zinc)?

P Put some oil on top of some water in a thin tray. This resembles an 'oil slick' at sea. Explore ways of dispersing the slick (so it will not harm seabirds or pollute beaches).

Q 'Liver salts' are used to cure acid stomach and hangovers. Find out what you can about them.

 Safety note

Nickel sulphate is harmful.

R When a solution of copper sulphate is electrolysed, copper is plated on the cathode. When a solution of nickel sulphate is electrolysed, nickel is plated on the cathode. What do you think will happen at the cathode when a solution containing a mixture of copper sulphate and nickel sulphate is electrolysed?
Design and carry out an experiment to test your prediction.

 Safety note

Only smell chlorine very carefully.

S When a solution of sodium choride is electrolysed, chlorine is produced at the anode.
Get together with your friends to explore what happens at the anode when:

a The solution of sodium chloride is made gradually more dilute.

b A gradually increasing amount of sodium bromide solution is mixed with the sodium chloride solution.

 Safety note

Sodium hydroxide solution is irritant at concentrations between 0.2 M and 1 M.

c A gradually increasing amount of sodium hydroxide solution is added to the sodium chloride solution.
Summarize the results of all the groups.

Appendix 1 An alphabetical list of the more common elements and some of their properties

Name	Symbol	Discovered	Melts (°C)	Boils (°C)	Density (g/cm³)	RAM*	Description
aluminium	Al	1827	660	2640	2.7	27	(reactive) everyday metal
antimony	Sb	BC	630	1700	6.7	122	soft everyday metal
argon	Ar	1894	−189	−186	gas	40	nonmetal (noble gas)
arsenic	As	1250	sublimes	613	5.7	75	properties in between those of metal and nonmetal
barium	Ba	1808	710	1640	3.5	137	reactive metal
bromine	Br	1826	−7	58	3.1	80	red nonmetal
calcium	Ca	1808	850	1480	1.6	40	reactive metal
carbon	C	BC	sublimes	4800	2.2	12	black nonmetal
chlorine	Cl	1774	−101	−35	gas	35.5	pale green nonmetal
chromium	Cr	1797	1900	2670	7.2	52	everyday metal (TM)
cobalt	Co	1735	1490	2900	8.9	59	everyday metal (TM)
copper	Cu	BC	1080	2570	8.9	63.5	brown everyday metal (TM)
fluorine	F	1886	−240	−188	gas	19	pale yellow nonmetal
gold	Au	BC	1064	2800	19.3	197	yellow everyday metal (TM)
helium	He	1868	−270	−269	gas	4	nonmetal (noble gas)
hydrogen	H	1766	−259	−253	gas	1	nonmetal
iodine	I	1811	sublimes	183	4.9	127	dark purple nonmetal
iron	Fe	BC	1540	2900	7.9	56	everyday metal (TM)
krypton	Kr	1898	−157	−153	gas	84	nonmetal (noble gas)
lead	Pb	BC	327	1750	11.4	207	soft everyday metal
lithium	Li	1817	180	1330	0.5	7	reactive metal
magnesium	Mg	1808	650	1100	1.7	24	reactive metal
manganese	Mn	1774	1250	2000	7.4	55	everyday metal (TM)
mercury	Hg	BC	−39	357	13.6	201	everyday metal
neon	Ne	1898	−249	−246	gas	20	nonmetal (noble gas)
nickel	Ni	1751	1450	2800	8.9	59	everyday metal (TM)
nitrogen	N	1772	−210	−196	gas	14	nonmetal
oxygen	O	1774	−219	−183	gas	16	nonmetal
phosphorus	P	1669	44	280	1.8	31	nonmetal
platinum	Pt	1735	1770	4000	21.4	195	everyday metal (TM)
plutonium	Pu	1940	640	3200	19.8		radioactive metal (TM)
potassium	K	1807	64	760	0.9	39	reactive metal
radium	Ra	1898	700	1200	5.0		radioactive reactive metal
silicon	Si	1824	1410	2400	2.4	28	nonmetal
silver	Ag	BC	961	2200	10.5	108	everyday metal
sodium	Na	1807	98	890	1.0	23	reactive metal
strontium	Sr	1808	770	1380	2.6	88	reactive metal
sulphur	S	BC	113	445	2.1	32	yellow nonmetal
tin	Sn	BC	232	2600	7.3	204	soft everyday metal
titanium	Ti	1791	1670	3300	4.5	48	everyday metal (TM)
tungsten	W	1783	3400	6000	19.3	184	everyday metal (TM)
uranium	U	1841	1130	3800	19.0	238	radioactive metal (TM)
vanadium	V	1801	1900	3400	6.0	51	everyday metal (TM)
xenon	Xe	1898	−112	−108	gas	131	nonmetal (noble gas)
zinc	Zn	1746	419	910	7.1	65	everyday metal

* RAM = relative atomic mass

Notes on the Description column:
1 For the meanings of some of the words used, see Section 8.3.
2 Colours are only given for: gases which are not colourless and solids which are not grey.
3 TM= transition metal (see Chapter 15).

Appendix 2   The preparation of common gases, with their tests

Safety note

Hydrogen is explosive.

Safety note

Many dilute acids are irritants. (see p 69)

Gas	Preparation	Test	Observation
oxygen (Section 3.8)	1. Run hydrogen peroxide solution on to black manganese oxide (Fig A.1). The manganese oxide *catalyses* (helps) the decomposition of the hydrogen peroxide to give oxygen.	glowing splint	splint rekindles
carbon dioxide (Section 3.9)	1. Run dilute hydrochloric acid on to marble chips (Fig A.2).	limewater	limewater turns milky
hydrogen (Section 10.5)	Run dilute sulphuric acid on to granulated zinc (Fig A.3).	lighted splint	burns, often with typical 'pop'
steam (water) (Section 3.6)		melting point boiling point cobalt chloride paper anhydrous copper sulphate	0 °C 100 °C blue to pale pink white to blue

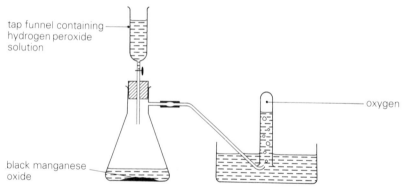

Fig A.1 The preparation of oxygen.

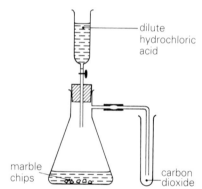

Fig A.2 The preparation of carbon dioxide.

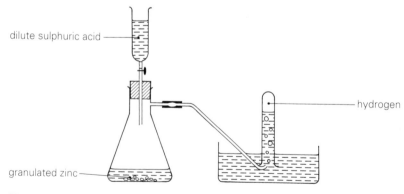

Fig A.3 The preparation of hydrogen.

Appendix 3   The position of common metals in the affinity series

Metal	Action of air	Action of water	Action of dilute acid	Action on oxide of carbon	hydrogen	Method of extraction from ore
potassium sodium calcium magnesium aluminium zinc iron tin lead copper mercury silver gold	burn readily to form oxides	react with cold water to give metal hydroxide	violent reactions **(danger)**	no reaction	no reaction	electrolysis of molten compound
		react with steam to give metal oxide and hydrogen	react to form salt plus hydrogen	reduction occurs at high temperatures	some reduction	chemical reduction of ore (often using carbon)
	react slowly to form ↓oxides	no reaction	no reaction	reduction occurs at 'Bunsen temperatures'	reduction occurs	
	no reaction			heating, on its own, decomposes these oxides		occur native

The position of carbon – at 'Bunsen temperatures' (up to about 800 °C) it comes between tin and iron. As the temperature is raised, carbon is capable of reducing the oxides of metals higher in the series.
The position of hydrogen – hydrogen is on a very similar level to iron. Thus iron reacts with steam, but hydrogen has some reaction with iron oxide as well.

Appendix 4   The Periodic Table

Appendix 5

The meaning of some important words often used in chemistry

Words in *italics* are themselves mentioned in the list.
A – adjective; N – noun; V – verb.

acid, N (or A); a sour substance with a *pH* less than 7, containing hydrogen which can be replaced by a metal.

affinity, N: the 'liking' of one element for another. Usually met in the 'affinity of metals for oxygen' leading to the **affinity series.**

alkali, N (A – **alkaline**): a *base* which is soluble in water. A substance which will *neutralize* an *acid* and which has a *pH* greater than 7.

alkali metal, N: a metal in *Group I* of the *Periodic Table*, that forms a soluble *alkaline* oxide.

alkaline earth metal, N: a metal in *Group II* of the *Periodic Table*, that forms a slightly soluble *alkaline* oxide.

alloy, N: a mixture of two or more *metals*.

analysis, N: finding out what a substance is.

anhydrous, A: without water. Used to describe *salts* which are not *hydrated*.

anode, N: the positive *electrode* in *electrolysis*.

atom, N: the smallest particle in an *element*.

base , N (A – **basic**): a substance which will *neutralize* an *acid*. Some bases are insoluble in water, others are soluble and called *alkalis*.

biodegradable, A: can be broken down biologically.

burning, N: the combination of a substance with oxygen, accompanied by flame.

boiling point, N: the temperature at which a substance turns from a liquid to a gas.

catalyst, N: a substance which speeds up a chemical reaction but which turns back into the same substance afterwards.

cathode, N: the negative *electrode* in *electrolysis*.

chemical reaction, N: a process in which the *products* are different chemicals from the *reactants*.

chromatography, N: a method of separating substances using a moving *solvent*.

combustion, N: the combination of a substance with oxygen.

compound, N: two or more *elements* chemically combined together.

condensation, N: a gas turning into a liquid.

decomposition, N: a *chemical reaction* in which a *compound* breaks down into simpler substances, usually as a result of being heated.

density, N: the mass of a particular volume of a substance. Usually measured in g/cm^3 or kg/m^3.

displacement, N: the 'pushing out' of a metal from one of its *salts* by another *metal*.

distillate, N: the result of *distillation*.

distillation, N: the *evaporation* and *condensation* of a liquid. Used to separate the *solvent* from a *solution*.

dissolving, N: the process by which a *solution* is formed.

electrochemical series, N: a list of *metals*, arranged in order of the voltages they produce when placed in pairs in an *electrolyte*.

electrode, N: a conducting rod by which the current enters or leaves an *electrolyte*.

electrolysis, N: the *decomposition* of a substance caused by an electric current.

electrolyte, N: the substance which is decomposed in *electrolysis*.

element, N: a substance which cannot be broken down into a simpler substance by chemical means.

evaporation, N: the process of turning a liquid into a gas.

fermentation, N: the reaction of sugars with water in the presence of yeast. The products are carbon dioxide and ethanol.

fertilizer, N: a substance added to the soil which replaces the chemicals used up by the plants.

filtrate, N: the clear liquid resulting from *filtration*.

filtration, N: the process of removing the solid particles from a *suspension* using a 'sieve'.

flame test, N: recognizing certain metals in *salts* using the colour they give to the flame.

flammable, A: catches fire easily.

fossil fuel, A, N: a fuel that has developed (from once-living material) underground over a period of very many years.

fractional distillation, N: the separation of a mixture of liquids by *distilling* off those with different *boiling points* at different times.

fraction, N: a mixture of liquids which have *boiling points* within a small range of temperature, produced as a result of *fractional distillation*.

freeze, V: turn from a liquid into a solid.

fuel, N: a substance which can be burned to release energy.

glass, N: a transparent mixture of oxides.

group, N: a vertical column in the *Periodic Table*, containing *elements* with similar properties.

halogen, N: a reactive nonmetal in *Group* VII of the *Periodic Table*.

hard water, A, N: water that does not cause a lather with soap. It contains dissolved calcium or magnesium *salts*.

hydrated, A: describes a *salt* which has water as part of its chemical structure.

igneous, A: describes rocks formed by cooling molten lava.

insoluble, A: describes a substance which will not *dissolve* in a certain *solvent*.

immiscible, A: describes two liquids which stay as two layers when shaken together.

indicator, N: anything which 'indicates' – often used of substances which are different colours in *acids* and *alkalis*.

malleable, A: describes a *metal's property* of being flexible and able to bend without breaking.

melt, V: change from solid to liquid. The temperature at which this occurs is called the **melting point**.

metals, N: a name given to one set of *elements*. They can be recognized by their *properties* (particularly: shiny when cut, *malleable*, form oxides which are *bases*).

metamorphic, A: describes rocks which have been changed from their original form by high temperature or pressure.

mineral, N: naturally occurring substance of which rocks are made.

mixture, N: substances which are just mixed together, not chemically combined.

molecule, N: two or more *atoms* chemically combined together.

native, A: describes the state of an *element* which is found in rocks as the *element* itself, rather than as a *compound*.

neutralization, N: a reaction in which an *acid* and a *base* react together to form a *salt* and water.

nonmetal part: the part of a *salt* which is not a *metal*: for example, chloride or sulphate.

ore, N: a solid *mineral* from which a *metal* can be obtained.

oxidation, N: the reaction of a substance with oxygen.

period, N: a horizontal row in the *Periodic Table*.

Periodic Table, A, N: an arrangement of *elements* in order of ascending *RAM*.

permanent change, A, N: a change which cannot easily be reversed.

pH: a scale of numbers describing *acidity* and *alkalinity*. pH 7 is described as neutral. *Acids* have *pH* values below 7 and *alkalis* have *pH* values greater than 7.

photosynthesis, N: the process by which carbon dioxide and water, in the presence of light, form carbohydrates and oxygen.

pollute, V: to contaminate with harmful impurities.

precipitate, N: a solid substance which is produced rapidly when two clear *solutions* are mixed.

product, N: the result of a *chemical reaction*.

properties, N: a description of a substance and how it behaves..
  physical properties include *density, melting point* and *malleability*.
  chemical properties describe the *chemical reactions* of a substance.

pure substance, A, N: a single *element* or *compound*. All of it will *melt* at the same temperature.

RAM, (**relative atomic mass**), N: the mass of an *atom* relative to that of hydrogen.

reactant, N: a substance which takes part in a *chemical reaction*.

recycle, V: to reuse a material to make the original article again.

reduction, N: the removal of oxygen from a substance.

residue, N: something which is left behind. Usually either what remains on a filter paper after *filtration* or what is left after a substance has been heated.

respiration, N: the process in which oxygen (which is breathed in) reacts with food to produce carbon dioxide and water (which can be breathed out).

salt, N: a compound which can be formed as the result of a *neutralization* reaction.

saturated solution, A, N: a *solution* in which no more *solute* will *dissolve*.

sedimentary, A: describes rocks formed by the settling of tiny particles.

solute, N: a substance which *dissolves* in a *solvent*. It is said to be **soluble**.

solution, N: a liquid which has a solid (or another liquid) mixed with it. The particles are too small to be seen.

solvent, N: a liquid in which certain other substances *dissolve*.

sublime, V: to turn straight from solid to gas.

suspension, N: a mixture of solid particles in a liquid which will settle out if left for a while.

vapour, N: a gas which can easily be *condensed* to a liquid.

volatile, A: describes a substance which has a low *boiling point*.

viscous, A: sticky, treacly.

Index